THE MARIA THUN BIODYNAMIC CALENDAR 2017

CREATED BY
MARIA AND MATTHIAS THUN

Floris Books

Compiled by Matthias Thun
Translated by Bernard Jarman
Additional astronomical material
by Wolfgang Held and Christian Maclean

Published in German under the title *Aussaattage*
English edition published by Floris Books

© 2016 Aussaattage-Verlag Thun & Thun OHG
English version © 2016 Floris Books

British Library CIP Data available

ISBN 978-178250-331-6
ISSN: 2052-5761

Printed in Poland

Contents

Walter Thun, Idyllic Spring, *oil, 48 x 69 cm, 1980*

Walter Thun's *Idyllic Spring*

If we spend some time thinking about this picture, we might feel like changing its title. The spring is only a small part of it – indeed, the central spring itself is almost hidden – and there is such manifold life here that we can almost feel ourselves transported to an early time of creation.

The glorious plant world covers the bare rocks, there's a frog which is closely tied to the watery element, and a lizard and curious snake to round off the image. Looking into the almost invisible cavern of the spring we can see a snail that lives entirely in water, and what appears to be a stone, but could also be a shell.

The entire cosmos is also incorporated into this painting. All kinds of stars can be found and in the background, the Moon so intimately linked to the movement of water and life, is patiently waiting.

Introduction

The emphasis in this year's calendar is on astronomical questions and how they relate to plant growth.

During an *opposition,* forces stream into the plant world from the constellations in which the two opposing luminaries are standing. Since constellations of a similar type are never opposite one another, a definitive effect of an opposition cannot be determined. If, for instance, one planet is in the Flower constellation of Libra, and another in Aries which is a Warmth-Fruit constellation, there is a mixed effect. It might be possible to identify one or the other influence after the event, but to predict with certainty is almost impossible.

With *trines* it is quite a different matter: their effects can often be seen in the way plants grow over time. Pages 25–27 give more details of this.

A third kind of effect comes about through *conjunctions* – when one luminary meets or passes by another. There is almost no positive influence on plant growth from conjunctions. Their effect becomes stronger if they are so close that the Moon or Sun covers a planet as seen from the Earth; astronomers call this an *occultation.* (In theory a planet can occlude another, but this is extremely rare, the last one was in 1818, the next in 2065). An occultation by the Moon can be observed, but one by the Sun cannot be seen. Sceptics often claim that these occultations cannot have any effect. When sowing trials are carried out during the period of an occultation, however, the missing influence of the occluded planet can subsequently be observed. It is as if the usual influence of the planet is 'blocked' when the Moon or Sun moves in front of it.

Another common misconception is that an occultation (or any other aspect of planets) occurs for a very limited period, such that a calculation given for Britain in GMT, for example, cannot have any effect in other parts of the world. This is a misunderstanding. All the aspects given are valid across the whole world, and a conjunction shown as taking place at 10^h GMT takes place at the same time in Moscow or in New York (even though it will be 14^h local time in Moscow and 5^h in New York).

Some years ago the International Astronomical Union demoted Pluto to 'dwarf planet', as it was deemed to be too small to be a real planet. However, plants seem to be unaware of this reclassification and continue to respond to its influences, which are no less significant than those of the larger planets. All the planets bring their own particular influence to bear on plant growth and on the weather. This is most noticeable when their influence has been blocked by an occultation, for example causing a deformation of the fruit.

For those interested in following the specific aspects of the planets during 2017, we are listing them in terms of number:
– 18 occultations (marked ☌)
– 14 planetary oppositions of Water-Earth constellations
– 18 planetary oppositions of Light-Warmth constellations
Additionally there are
– 9 Light (Flower) trines (marked ▲)
– 12 Water (Leaf) trines (marked ▲)
– 8 Warmth (Fruit) trines (marked ▲)
– 6 Earth (Root) trines (marked ▲)

The large number of trines in 2017 have a marked effect on plant growth, and our calendar shows how to make use of these influences.

Review of 2014 to 2016 and the Year Ahead

In our part of Germany, 2014 was a textbook year. An extended and uninterrupted spring, followed by a good summer and autumn, ensured a good harvest for farmers and gardeners. Bees also gathered so much nectar from flowers right through into the autumn that we had the highest yield of honey for many years. While winter did not see real cold or significant snowfalls, it was still clearly wintry.

The following year, 2015, started in a similar way but did not progress as we might have hoped. And 2016 has been really difficult. Spring started well, but beekeepers who had harvested honey during the spring flush had to return some. Although there was a reasonable honey flow in the summer, the continual change from hot to cooler weather meant that the bees had to use a lot of their stored honey. While in 2015 there was plenty of blossom honey to see the bees through the winter, this will probably not be the case in 2016. They will need to be given sugar together with the herb teas we recommend.

The first part if 2016 was also difficult in the garden and on the fields. Cool and watery influences were so strong that they affected hay and grain harvests.

Looking at 2017, the planets show an ambiguous pattern. In the first half of the year, influences from the constellation of Leo (which brings Warmth and Fruit influence) are missing. They only appear in the second half of the year to help the fruit and seed harvest in the northern hemisphere. In the southern hemisphere the Leo influences are less significant, and we need to look to the constellations of Sagittarius and Aries for that influence in spring and autumn.

We feel that at least the first half of 2017 will be dominated by cold and damp.

A History of Biodynamics

In recent years there has been a growing interest in lunar rhythms, so we shall take a brief look at the history of biodynamics in order to understand how this has come about.

For centuries, old farming wisdom was passed down, sometimes with little real understanding, but sufficient for subsistence living. Then in the nineteenth century the chemist Justus von Liebig (1803–73) changed the direction of agriculture. His research into plant nutrients led him to add certain elements – particularly nitrogen – to the soil, which led to significant increases in yields.

This new approach was widely embraced, but also meant a departure from the accepted principle of using compost and manure to improve soil fertility. Instead, manuring was seen as a way of feeding plants. Over time this led to a decline in soil quality and sometimes serious deficiency symptoms. Liebig recognised the problem, and in his 1844 *Chemische Briefe* (Letters on Chemistry) urged farmers not to ignore soil fertility. His plea was largely ignored, however, and today he's known as the 'father of the fertiliser industry'.

By 1924, soil conditions had degraded so much that a number of farmers approached Rudolf Steiner, the founder of anthroposophy, for help. The health and quality of their crops and livestock had deteriorated as a result of using chemical fertiliser. Steiner's subsequent Agriculture Course addressed how to

Mulching green manure

bring vitality to soil, and became the basis for biodynamic agriculture. A key principle is that fertilising means bringing life to the soil – to the earthy constituents of the soil.

From small beginnings, biodynamic agriculture spread rapidly after the Second World War. It has become an important ingredient in European agriculture and is now practiced in at least sixty countries around the world. The popularity of organic methods also increased dramatically in that time. But Steiner's biodynamic recommendations are not so easily understood; he repeatedly emphasised the importance of taking local conditions – including soil, climate, vegetation, animals and people – into account. It's not a one-size-fits-all approach and it requires an individual connection to the farm or garden.

Maria Thun's work

In the 1940s Maria Thun, who had grown up on a farm, came across the Agriculture Course. Much of its content reminded her of her father's old methods, and she resolved to test these new ideas. She was particularly struck by the idea that the growth of plants was related to the movement of stars and planets. She had heard of this from her parents, and the idea was self-evident to her. However, her parents' methods seemed rather imprecise, so she began systematic planting trials in 1952 and over the years published her results. After other practitioners had assessed her trials and corroborated her results, she felt confident enough to publish an annual sowing calendar from 1962.

Compost trials

Full Moon   *First visible crescent after New Moon*

It is well known that our planting trials have taken place, and will continue to take place, in biodynamic soil. In the late 1960s and 1970s Maria Thun was asked whether her results would also hold true in conventionally treated soil. Subsequent trials in our own fields (which had recently expanded) alongside conventional trials at agricultural colleges found that, provided certain basic agricultural rules were observed, the effects of the stars hold true for *all* plant growth.

In these trials we were of course reminded of Liebig's plea to farmers that particular attention be paid to the humus content of the soil and we saw to it that special consideration was given to the building up of humus. If a lot of fresh manure or plant material such as from green manure is applied directly to the soil, a high raw humus content will be achieved which is only partly available to plants. In order for humus to be biologically active it needs to either be composted or carefully worked into the soil in such a way that microorganisms are activated (see Further Reading, p.64, for detailed sources of information on the different forms of composting). To encourage microorganisms, earthworms and other soil fauna, muck should be spread on the green manure before turning it in. It should then be left to wither and dry out for a day or two and then turned lightly into the top soil. Once the green manure has been incorporated, three applications of barrel preparation can be given to support its transformation and to build soil humus. After a week or two it may then be ploughed in deeper. If the green manure isn't allowed to dry before being ploughed in, soil organisms may not be able to cope. In heavy soils it could then be many months before it can be processed by soil organisms, making good humus formation very hard to achieve. Done correctly, though, this approach can improve almost any soil, regardless of subsequent farming systems, and make it accessible to the influences of lunar constellations.

We found in our composting trials that the soil needs to contain at least 1.1% available humus for planetary and lunar influences to take effect. If the humus content is lower, these effects do not show. However, it is not only the humus content but also how water is dealt with, that determines how effective the lunar constellations will be. Indeed, most people know that the Moon is linked with tidal rhythms and not only is there a (half) daily rhythm of high and low tides, but there is monthly rhythm of particularly high tides (spring tides) around New Moon and Full Moon, and less extreme tides (neap tides) around the Half Moons.

What is special about this calendar?

The growing interest in lunar rhythms has seen many different lunar calendars spring up, and the *Maria Thun Biodynamic Calendar* is often lumped in with them. However, we don't consider this to be simply a lunar calendar because we look at both lunar *and* planetary influences. It may help new readers to explore this in a bit more detail; we hope that long-standing readers will bear with us.

Let's first of all revisit the effects of the Moon itself. Our earliest trials showed that the moon operates in different areas. One of these has to do with the watery element and is connected to the *phase* of the moon (Full Moon, waxing, waning, etc.). The Moon also acts as mediator for the *zodiac constellation* in which it is positioned. Here the phase is of only minor importance. The moon's phases are of special interest to the observer since they can be followed in the sky. To the soil and plants however their importance is minimal.

We might imagine that constellation effects are continually being mediated by the Moon, and that plants are therefore continually under their influence. Although this is partly true, plants can only fully respond to and process these

Heavy sprinkling, if used sensibly, should take place at night

Broad beans

influences if the soil in which they are growing has simultaneously been moved. This soil movement activates the microorganisms and they in turn give the plants a new orientation that enables them to respond to the current zodiacal influence. This fine and seemingly subtle action of the microorganisms, however, only occurs if the humus in the soil is in the right condition for the plants and is accessible to them.

The zodiacal influence of the Moon can be suppressed when too much fertiliser is applied (of either organic or inorganic origin) or by excessive irrigation. The soil organisms are then overwhelmed and only the moon's phases have any influence on the plants.

Let's now consider the effects of the planets. They also influence plant growth and weather, separately from the Moon. Seen from the Earth, they too wander through the zodiac and communicate what lives in the different constellations. In this case, however, it is coupled with the planet's own influence. If for example Neptune, which has a watery nature, moves through a Water constellation such as Cancer, its watery influence is magnified. Similarly if Venus, which carries light characteristics, passes through the Light constellation of Gemini, there will be a strong Light and Flower influence.

We can see therefore, it is not only the Moon that rules and mediates what occurs in the heavens but that all the planets work harmoniously together making it possible for human beings to intervene constructively in the process.

We should also briefly mention the effects of the Sun. Seen from the Earth, the Sun is also a wandering luminary. It gives us, of course, our two fundamental rhythms of day and night, and the seasons of the year. But it can also be thought of as a grand master working as the conductor of our cosmos. Steiner suggested that the Sun's character changes according to the constellation in which it stands. It would then be called a Gemini Sun, a Cancer Sun, and so on. And here's one quick example of the Sun's effects: beans such as broad beans are often attacked by aphids when there is a change in weather. By planting broad beans at Fruit times when the Sun is in the constellation of Aquarius, aphid attacks can be reduced.

A major difference between the *Maria Thun Biodynamic Calendar* and other lunar calendars is that others usually work with regular astrological *signs,* whereas this calendar uses the visible astronomical *constellations.* (The relationship between the signs and constellations is shown on p. 24.) This is significant because the visible constellations vary in size, and are not in the same positions as the signs. For that reason the dates given in this calendar are different from those of the fixed-length astrological signs. The importance of using the visible constellations for sowing and planting times has been confirmed in numerous trials over several decades.

For the astronomical data shown in this calendar we are of course dependent on various astronomical ephemerides, and each year the position of Sun, Moon and planets in relation to the constellations of the zodiac used here has to be calculated anew. For the English editions, the Central European Time given in the German calendar is converted to GMT or Eastern Standard/Daylight Time (for the North American version).

The Effect of the Sun on Plant Growth

Maria Thun

This and the following two articles were written some years ago but they relate directly to the theme of this calendar.

The Sun gives the Earth its two main rhythms of day and night, and of the seasons of the year. As well as showing which constellation the Moon is in, we also show the date when the Sun moves from one zodiac constellation to another. (Remember that these dates relate to the visible astronomical constellations, not to the astrological signs; for more information, see p. 24.)

Carrots

It's well known that the Earth rotates around its axis once every 24 hours, and that the stars of the zodiac can therefore be seen from any point on Earth, assuming it's not the daytime – when the Sun outshines them – or a cloudy night. If we look at the stars on a clear night at intervals of one or two hours, we can become aware of how they move steadily forwards. This east to west movement reflects the Earth's rotation and in 24 hours completes a full 360° circuit.

Rapeseed

Sunflower

False flax   Linseed

There is also a slower counter-movement of about 1° per day because of the Earth's annual revolution around the Sun.

Although the stars are not visible during the day, it is possible to calculate exactly which constellation is behind the Sun. At his observatory on the island of Hven, the great astronomer Tycho Brahe had a deep shaft sunk into the earth with a tall tower built above, so that he was able to observe a tiny portion of the sky during daytime, because all the sunlight was cut out. This greatly aided his astronomical observations.

The effect of the Sun on soil, and therefore plant growth, shouldn't be underestimated. In early editions of this calendar we presented results from trials that showed how soil composition subtly changes when the Sun moves from one constellation to another, because of a change in the activity of microorganisms in the soil. Soil analysis can give some indication of these changes.

Research by the microbiologist Erhard Ahrens has shown that nitrogen fixing bacteria (azotobacter) are especially active in the soil when the Sun is in particular constellations. Nitrogen fixation reaches its peak in May and September in the northern hemisphere, and in January and February in the southern hemisphere. This clearly indicates that nitrogen fixation is stimulated when the Sun is in the constellations of Taurus (May 14 – June 21) and Virgo (Sep 16 – Nov 1) and Capricorn (Jan 20 – Feb 15). The bacteria appear to rest during the times in between. Field trials and laboratory experiments have shown that when the Moon passes through these same constellations (two days in Capricorn, two days in Taurus, four days in Virgo) both the decomposing bacteria and nitrogen fixing azotobacter are significantly more active than at other times. It is as if the Moon's path through the zodiac and its effect is a kind of reflection of the Sun's.

The effect of the Sun in different constellations can also be found in cultivated plants. It was well known, for instance, to traditional farmers that oats and

Traditional grains for seed production

field beans sown in the second half of February or the first half of March – when the Sun is in the constellation of Aquarius – produce the most healthy plants and best yields. Beans sown later, when the Sun is in Pisces, are likely to attract aphids, while oats are more susceptible to fungal infections.

Carrots are similarly affected by the Sun's position in the zodiac. If they are sown when the Sun is in Pisces, their leaves grow rampant and the crowns have a tendency to turn green, both of which result in a poor flavour. If they are sown when the Sun is in Aries, they barely grow and are soon overrun by weeds. However, if they're sown when the Sun is in Taurus (April – May), early growth is rapid and the carrots are able to ripen in autumn. The Virgo Sun stimulates sugar formation and ripens the protein so that the carrots have a low nitrate content.

Plants grown for their oil such as rapeseed and sunflowers are also influenced by the Sun's position in the zodiac. Winter rape thrives best when sown with the Sun in Leo, spring sown oil crops are best sown when the Sun is in Aries (March – April) as this is a Warmth constellation. For their further cultivation and to encourage the productaion of oil, times when the Moon is in Light constellations should be chosen.

As a final word, it's interesting to note that earthworms are influenced by cosmic rhythms as well. This can be observed by counting the number of worms present at different soil depths. When the Moon is in Aries, Leo and Sagittarius, the majority of worms are at a depth of 100–120 cm (40–48 in); when the

Moon is in Taurus, Virgo or Capricorn, they're at 5–20 cm (2–8 in); and when the Moon is in Pisces, Cancer or Scorpio, they rise up to about 5 cm (2 in), even coming out of the ground overnight to wriggle on paths.

Maximising Plant Fertility and Nutritional Value

Maria Thun

The best nutrition is accomplished by making our farms and gardens receptive to the forces of the zodiac. Rudolf Steiner stated that 'the forces of the earth of the cosmos take effect through earthly substances' and so in this article we shall explore how that works in practice.

Cultivated plants have a capacity for producing nutritive substances including proteins, fats and carbohydrates. They also have a natural ability to reproduce, whether through seeds, or asexually like strawberries and potatoes. But there has been a gradual decline in fertility since the start of the twentieth century, which was one of the reasons that farmers asked for Rudolf Steiner's help and led to his Agriculture Course. Steiner stated that a plant's reproductive power comes from the inferior planets (Moon, Mercury, Venus) but that its nutritional qualities come from the superior plants (Mars, Jupiter, Saturn).

In grain crops, the two aspects are of course intimately linked in seed formation. Steiner indicated that regenerative power is stimulated by sowing crops 'close to winter', whereas sowing further away from winter improves their nutritional qualities. Sowing close to winter does not necessarily mean during the Christmas period as is often suggested. The old farmers referred to late sowings as 'Advent grains'. The constellation best suited to grain sowing is Sagittarius. Nowadays the Sun enters in Sagittarius around December 19 (which still leaves five days of Advent for sowing!), but before about AD 200 Christmas fell in Capricorn, and it was over the four weeks preceding December 25 that the Sun was in Sagittarius – hence the name 'Advent grains'.

We started late-sowing trials in 1963, sowing rye daily throughout December and January. If the ground was frozen, we laid the seed on top and covered it with chaff; if there was snow, we sowed into the snow. The results varied; some of the plants sown in the first half of December (while the Sun was in Scorpio) suffered fungal attacks in spring when the Sun entered Pisces. Sowings made when the Sun moved into Capricorn (around January 20) tillered well but did not come into ear; they need a further growing period in order to form seeds.

Incidentally, when I showed my father – by then almost ninety years old – the results of these trials, he told me that his father had been a 'sower'. He always

Walter Thun, The Twelvefold Human Being, *Pen and ink*

sowed grain, not only on his own farm but also on neighbouring farms, during Advent, a task he later passed on to his son. After the First World War the idea was frowned upon and few farmers asked my father to sow Advent grain. The new fertilising techniques made such considerations irrelevant.

We continued our sowing trials for three years, always growing a crop from the saved seeds the year after. Other biodynamic researchers like Erika Windeck, Martin Schmidt and Erhard Breda were conducting similar trials. They were apparently searching for 'good Full Moon sowings'. Their experience led them to conclude however that the midwinter New Moon provided the best conditions for the next year's seeds. They were of course only looking at the phase of the Moon, not its position in the zodiac. We were able to share our findings with them, namely that first-class seed was produced when both Sun and Moon were in Sagittarius (although we also had good results when the Sun was in Sagittarius and the Moon in Aries or Leo).

Martin Schmidt, with whom we communicated regularly, had felt Virgo to be the ideal constellation for grain; it is after all associated with the goddess Demeter who holds an ear of grain – the star of Spica – in her hand. Afterwards Schmidt started to explore other zodiac influences as well.

Erika Windeck later undertook sowing trials with wall barley and rye brome, and we often compared results. We also discussed these issues with Theodor Schwenk, Agnes Fyfe, Suso Vetter, Rudolf Hauschka, Udo Renzenbrinck, Walter Bühler, Wilhelm Pelikan and others.

Returning to the question regarding the influence of phases of the Moon, it's interesting to study rice, a plant intimately connected with water and grown in paddy fields. A strong connection to lunar phases in this case would make sense. Lili Kolisko did a lot of research into Moon phases and concluded that two extreme situations were possible. If the Full Moon influence is too powerful the crop has a tendency to rot; if the New Moon influence is too strong there is a tendency towards lignification, for becoming woody. Our experience over decades has born this out, although it's worth remembering that Rudolf Steiner stated clearly that plants should grow in enlivened soil, not enlivened water.

If our soils are truly enlivened in this way the Moon is able to not only work on earthly substances through its phases, but is able like the planets to act as mediator for the more distant forces of the twelve constellations of the zodiac. If we can harness that power through our care of the soil, we should be able to produce nutritional food for human beings which will in turn nourish the body in its twelvefold nature. In this way, eating can itself become an act of creation.

Best Practice for Harvesting and Storing Seed

Maria Thun

If we do manage to care for our soil in a way that allows the cosmic forces to work through it, we are faced with the issue of seed quality. The ability to genetically modify plants has raised many questions about seed plants and biodiversity in recent years. A number of different seed initiatives have emerged in recent years dedicated to the preservation of old varieties or the selection of new ones. Results have been mixed due to differing approaches – some remain committed to observing lunar phases while others focus on different kinds of manuring.

Since plant breeding is a complex and difficult undertaking, we would like to focus on the producton of already existing good quality seed varieties. Root vegetables make an excellent case study because their reproduction is relatively simple. The easiest to produce seed from are radishes. They work well because, if sown early enough, they can produce seed by late autumn. The plants need to be thoroughly dried before threshing.

A basic rule for good seed production is to allow the plant to grow until it has begun to develop the desired fruiting body. In the case of a root plant this is of course the root. (A leaf plant like salad needs to develop a head; tomatoes or

A clamp of beets showing leaf stems

cucumbers need to show the beginnings of these fruits, similarly with flowers, and so on.) Once that has happened, the approach is then changed and all subsequent cultivations and spraying should be carried out at Fruit times in order to support good seed development. Harvesting should be done at Root times.

If seed is to be collected the following year from carrots, beetroot or turnips, they will need to be stored over winter. A cool cellar is suitable for this purpose; if a large quantity of roots is to be stored, use a clamp outdoors. The clamp should be covered with straw. Rye straw is ideal because it doesn't degrade easily, even when it's on the ground. Finally, cover the straw with 20 cm (8 in) of soil; in areas with high snowfall or cold frosts, spruce or fir branches can also be laid on top to provide an air cushion for extra insulation. Smaller quantities of roots (as well as apples and pears) can be stored over winter in the barn or a loft with a covering of straw.

A good seed head needs to develop from the roots when they are planted in spring. Care should therefore be taken to leave 3–4 cm (1–1½ in) of the old leaves attached when cutting off the tops. Leaves may also be twisted off but again take care not to damage the crown. If this happens (as is frequently the case with mechanised harvesting) several small flower shoots are likely to develop around the edges of the cut with no central shoot being formed. This affects the quality of the seed. Secondary roots should not be removed. Seeding shoots that have started to form in the first year should not be used. Their seeds are not

Twisted off leaves; the leaf core of a carrot is clearly visible

Beetroot with twisted off leaves and visible leaf core

Carrot inflorescence, unusable for seeds as it is from the first year

Carrot flower

Carrot inflorescence

Carrot seeds

Beetroot

Beetroot inflorescence

Beetroot infructescence

much use and will result in poor quality fruits. Intensively bred industrial juicing carrots are also unsuitable for seed and have often lost the typical carrot flavour.

The roots which would have been harvested in the autumn at Root times should be replanted in spring at Fruit times to encourage them to invest their strength in seed production. For the best quality, choose times when the Moon is in Leo. The fully grown seed heads should be harvested at Root times once the seed has ripened. The seeds will then grow good roots the following year.

Fodder beet

Fodder beet infructescence

Background to the Calendar

The zodiac

The **zodiac** is a group of twelve constellations of stars which the Sun, Moon and all the planets pass on their circuits. The Sun's annual path always takes exactly the same line, called **ecliptic.** The Moon's and planets' paths vary slightly, sometimes above and sometimes below the ecliptic. The point at which their paths cross the ecliptic is called a **node** (☊ and ☋).

The angles between the Sun, Moon and planets are called **aspects.** In this calendar the most important is the 120° angle, or **trine.**

In the illustration below the outer circle shows the varying sizes of the visible **constellations** of the **zodiac.** The dates on this outer circle are the days on which the Sun enters the constellation (this can change by one day because of leap years). The inner circle shows the divisions into equal sections of 30° corresponding to the **signs** used in astrology.

It is the *constellations,* not the signs, on which our observations are based, and which are used throughout this calendar.

The twelve constellations are grouped into four different types, each having three constellations at an angle of about 120°, or trine. About every nine days the Moon passes from one type, for instance Root, through the other types (Flower, Leaf and Fruit) and back to Root again.

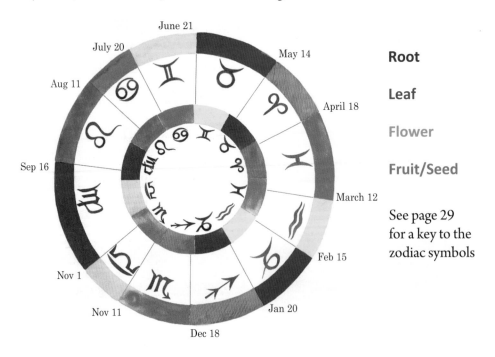

Root

Leaf

Flower

Fruit/Seed

See page 29 for a key to the zodiac symbols

If a New Moon is at a node there is a solar eclipse, as the Moon is directly in front of the Sun, while a Full Moon at a node causes a lunar eclipse where the Earth's shadow falls on the Moon. If the Sun or Moon pass exactly in front of a planet, there is an occultation (•). If Mercury or Venus pass exactly in front of the Sun, this is a transit (other planets cannot pass in front of the Sun).

What are oppositions, trines and conjunctions?
Oppositions ☍

A **geocentric** (Earth-centred) **opposition** occurs when for the observer on the Earth there are two planets opposite one another – 180° apart – in the heavens. They look at one another from opposite sides of the sky and their light interpenetrates. Their rays fall on to the Earth and stimulate in a beneficial way the seeds that are being sown in that moment. In our trials we have found that seeds sown at times of opposition resulted in a higher yield of top quality crops.

With a **heliocentric** (Sun-centred) **opposition** an observer would need to place themselves on the Sun. This is of course physically impossible but we can understand it through our thinking. The Sun is in the centre and the two planets placed 180° apart also gaze at each other but this time across the Sun. Their rays are also felt by the Earth and stimulate better plant growth. However, heliocentric oppositions are not shown or taken into account in the calendar.

At times of opposition two zodiac constellations are also playing their part. If one planet is standing in a Warmth constellation, the second one will usually be in a Light constellation or vice versa. If one planet is in a Water constellation, the other will usually be in an Earth one. (As the constellations are not equally sized, the point opposite may not always be in the opposite constellation.)

Trines △ or ▲

The twelve constellations are grouped into four different types, each having three constellations at an angle of about 120°, or trine. About every nine days the Moon passes a similar region of forces.

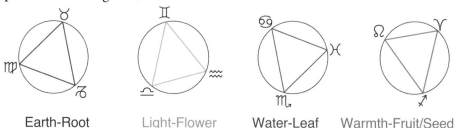

Earth-Root   Light-Flower   Water-Leaf   Warmth-Fruit/Seed

Trines occur when planets are 120° from one another. The two planets are then usually both standing in the same elemental configuration – Aries and Leo for example are both Warmth constellations. A Warmth trine means that the effects of these constellations will enhance fruit and seed formation in the plants sown at this time. If two planets are in trine position in Water, watery influences will be enhanced, which usually brings high rainfall. Plants sown on these days will yield more leaf than those on other days. Trine effects can change the way plants grow.

Conjunctions ☌

Conjunctions and multiple conjunctions occur when two or more planets stand behind one another in space. It is then usually only the planet closest to the Earth that has any influence on plant growth. If this influence is stronger than that of the sidereal Moon, cosmic disturbances can occur that irritate the plant and cause checks in growth. This negative effect is increased further when the Moon or another planet stands directly in front of another – an occultation (☉) or eclipse in the case of Sun and Moon. Sowing at these times will affect subsequent growth detrimentally and harm a plant's regenerative power.

The effects of the Moon

In its 27-day orbit round the Earth the Moon passes through the constellations of the zodiac and transmits forces to the Earth which affect the four elements: Earth, Light (Air), Water and Warmth (Fire). They in turn affect the four parts of the plant: the roots, the flower, the leaves and the fruit or seeds. The health and growth of a plant can therefore be stimulated by sowing, cultivating and harvesting it in tune with the cycles of the Moon.

These cosmic forces can also be harnessed in beekeeping. By opening and closing the bee 'skep' or box in rhythm with the Moon, the bees' activity is directly affected.

The table opposite summarises the effects of the movement of the Moon through the twelve constellations on plants, bees and the weather.

The amount of time the Moon spends in any constellation varies between two and four days. However, this basic framework can be disrupted by planetary oppositions which override the normal tendencies; equally, it may be that trine positions (see above) activate a different elemental force to the ones the Moon is transmitting. Times when the Moon's path or a planet's path intersects with the ecliptic (ascending ☊ or descending ☋ node; see page 24) are subject to mainly negative effects. These are intensified if there is an eclipse or occultation, in which case the nearer planet interrupts the influence of the distant one. Such days are unsuitable for sowing or harvesting.

Constellation	Sign	Element	Plant	Bees	Weather
Pisces, Fishes	♓ W	Water	Leaf	Making honey	Damp
Aries, Ram	♈ H	Warmth	Fruit	Gathering nectar	Warm/hot
Taurus, Bull	♉ E	Earth	Root	Building comb	Cool/cold
Gemini, Twins	♊ L	Light	Flower	Gathering pollen	Airy/bright
Cancer, Crab	♋ W	Water	Leaf	Making honey	Damp
Leo, Lion	♌ H	Warmth	Fruit	Gathering nectar	Warm/hot
Virgo, Virgin	♍ E	Earth	Root	Building comb	Cool/cold
Libra, Scales	♎ L	Light	Flower	Gathering pollen	Airy/bright
Scorpio, Scorpion	♏ W	Water	Leaf	Making honey	Damp
Sagittarius, Archer	♐ H	Warmth	Fruit	Gathering nectar	Warm/hot
Capricorn, Goat	♑ E	Earth	Root	Building comb	Cool/cold
Aquarius, Waterman	♒ L	Light	Flower	Gathering pollen	Airy/bright

Groupings of plants for sowing and harvesting

When we grow plants, different parts are cultivated for food. We can divide them into four groups.

Root crops at Root times

Radishes, swedes, sugar beet, beetroot, celeriac, carrot, scorzonera, etc., fall into the category of root plants. Potatoes and onions are included in this group too. Root times produce good yields and top storage quality for these crops.

Leaf plants at Leaf times

The cabbage family, lettuce, spinach, lambs lettuce, endive, parsley, leafy herbs and fodder plants are categorised as leaf plants. Leaf times are suitable for sowing and tending these plants but not for harvesting and storage. For this (as well as harvesting of cabbage for sauerkraut) Fruit and Flower times are recommended.

Flower plants at Flower times

These times are favourable for sowing and tending all kinds of flower plants but also for cultivating and spraying 501 (a biodynamic preparation) on oil-bearing plants such as linseed, rape, sunflower, etc. Cut flowers have the strongest scent and remain fresh for longer if cut at Flower times, and the mother plant will provide many new side shoots. If flowers for drying are harvested at Flower times they retain the most vivid colours. If cut at other times they soon lose their colour. Oil-bearing plants are best harvested at Flower times.

Fruit Plants at Fruit times

Plants that are cultivated for their fruit or seed belong to this category, including beans, peas, lentils, soya, maize, tomatoes, cucumber, pumpkin, zucchini, but also cereals for summer and winter crops. Sowing oil-bearing plants at Fruit times provides the best yields of seeds. The best time for extraction of oil later on is at Flower times. Leo times are particularly suitable to grow good seed. Fruit plants are best harvested at Fruit times. They store well and their seeds provide good plants for next year. When storing fruit, also remember to choose the time of the ascending Moon.

There is always uncertainty as to which category some plants belong (see list on p. 57). Onions and beetroot provide a similar yield when sown at Root and Leaf times, but the keeping quality is best from Root times. Kohlrabi and cauliflowers belong to Leaf times, as does Florence fennel. Broccoli is more beautiful and firmer when sown at Flower times.

Explanations of the Calendar Pages

Next to the date is the constellation (and time of entry) in which the Moon is positioned. This is the astronomical constellation, not the astrological sign (see p. 24). The next column shows solar and lunar events.

A further column shows which element is dominant on that day (this is useful for beekeepers). Note H is used for warmth (heat). Sometimes there is a change during the day; in this case, both elements are mentioned. Warmth effects on thundery days are implied but are not mentioned in this column, but may have a ♄ symbol in the far right 'Weather' column.

The next column shows in colour the part of the plant which will be enhanced by sowing or cultivation on that day. Numbers indicate times of day. On the extreme right, special events in nature are noted as well as anticipated weather changes which disturb or break up the overall weather pattern.

When parts of the plant are indicated that do not correspond to the Moon's position in the zodiac (often it is more than one part on the same day), it is not a misprint, but takes account of other cosmic aspects which overrule the Moon-zodiac pattern and have an effect on a different part of the plant.

Unfavourable times are marked thus ▓▓▓. These are caused by eclipses, nodal points of the Moon or the planets or other aspects with a negative influence; they are not elaborated upon in the calendar. If one has to sow at unfavourable times for practical reasons, one can choose favourable days for hoeing, which will improve the plant.

The position of the planets in the zodiac is shown in the box below, with the date of entry into a new constellation. R indicates the planet is moving retrograde (with the date when retrograde begins), D indicates the date when it moves in direct motion again.

On the opposite calendar page astronomical aspects are indicated. Those visible to the naked eye are shown in **bold** type. Visible conjunctions (particularly Mercury's) are not always visible from all parts of the Earth.

Astronomical symbols

Constellations		*Planets*		*Aspects*			
♓	Pisces	☉	Sun	☊	Ascending node	**St**	Storms likely
♈	Aries	☾, ☽	Moon	☋	Descending node	♄	Thunder likely
♉	Taurus	☿	Mercury	⌒	Highest Moon	**Eq**	Earthquakes
♊	Gemini	♀	Venus	⌣	Lowest Moon	**Tr**	Traffic dangers
♋	Cancer	♂	Mars	**Pg**	Perigee	**Vo**	Volcanic activity
♌	Leo	♃	Jupiter	**Ag**	Apogee		
♍	Virgo	♄	Saturn	☍	Opposition		Northern Transplanting Time
♎	Libra	♅	Uranus	☌	Conjunction		
♏	Scorpio	♆	Neptune	☄	Eclipse/occultation		
♐	Sagittarius	♇	Pluto	☄	Lunar eclipse		Southern Transplanting Time
♑	Capricorn	○	Full Moon	△	Trine (or ▲)		
♒	Aquarius	●	New Moon	E Earth L Light/Air W Water H Warmth/Heat			

Transplanting times

From midwinter through to midsummer the Sun rises earlier and sets later each day while its path across the sky ascends higher and higher. From midsummer until midwinter this is reversed, the days get shorter and the midday Sun shines from an ever lower point in the sky. This annual ascending and descending of the Sun creates our seasons. As it ascends and descends during the course of the year the Sun is slowly moving (from an Earth-centred point of view) through each of the twelve constellations of the zodiac in turn. On average it shines for one month from each constellation.

In the northern hemisphere the winter solstice occurs when the Sun is in the constellation of Sagittarius and the summer solstice when it is in Gemini. At any point from Sagittarius to Gemini the Sun is ascending, while from Gemini to Sagittarius it is descending. In the southern hemisphere this is reversed.

The Moon (and all the planets) follow approximately the same path as the Sun

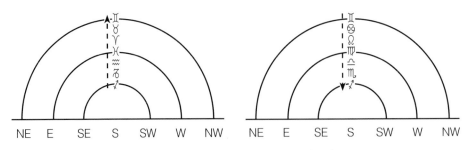

Northern hemisphere ascending Moon (left) and descending Moon (right): Transplanting Time

around the zodiac but instead of a year, the Moon takes only about 27½ days to complete one cycle, shining from each constellation in turn for a period of two to three days. This means that the Moon will ascend for about fourteen days and then descend.

It is important to distinguish the journey of the Moon through the zodiac (siderial rhythm) from the waxing and waning (synodic) cycle: in any given constellation there may be a waxing, waning, full, quarter, sickle or gibbous Moon. As it moves through the zodiac the Moon, like the Sun, is ascending (in the northern hemisphere) when it is in the constellations from Sagittarius to Gemini and descending from Gemini to Sagittarius. In the southern hemisphere it is ascending from Gemini to Sagittarius and descending from Sagittarius to Gemini.

When the Moon is ascending, plant sap rises more strongly. The upper part of the plant fills with sap and vitality. This is a good time for cutting scions (for grafting). Fruit harvested during this period remains fresh for longer when stored.

When the Moon is descending, plants take root readily and connect well with their new location. This period is referred to as the **Transplanting Time.** Moving plants from one location to another is called *transplanting.* This is the case when young plants are moved from the seed bed into their final growing position but also when the gardener wishes to strengthen the root development of young fruit trees, shrubs or pot plants by frequently re-potting them. Sap movement is slower during the descending Moon. This is why it is a good time for trimming hedges, pruning trees and felling timber as well as applying compost to meadows, pastures and orchards.

Note that sowing is the moment when a seed is put into the soil; either the ascending or descending period can be used. It then needs time to germinate and grow. This is different from *transplanting,* which is best done during the descending Moon. These times given in the calendar. **Northern Transplanting Times** refer to the northern hemisphere, and **Southern Transplanting Times** refer to the southern hemisphere. All other constellations and planetary aspects are equally valid in both hemispheres.

Local times

Times given are *Greenwich Mean Time* (GMT), using 24-hour clock with ^h after the time. Thus 15^h is 3 pm. **No account is taken of daylight saving (summer) time (DST).** Note 0^h is midnight at the beginning of a date, and 24^h is midnight at the end of the date.

Add (+) or subtract (−) times as below. For countries not listed check local time against GMT.

Europe

Britain, Ireland, Portugal: GMT
  (March 26 to Oct 28, +1^h for DST)
Iceland: GMT (no DST)
Central Europe: +1^h
  (March 26 to Oct 28, +2^h for DST)
Eastern Europe (Finland, etc.): +2^h
  (March 26 to Oct 28, +3^h for DST)
Russia (Moscow), Georgia: +4^h (no DST)

Africa/Asia

Namibia: + 1^h (to April 1 & from
  Sep 3, + 2^h for DST)
South Africa: + 2^h (no DST)
Kenya: add 3^h (no DST)
Egypt: add 2^h (June 30 to Oct 26, +3^h
  for DST)
Israel: add 2^h (March 24 to Oct 28, +3^h
  for DST)
India: add 5½^h (no DST)
Philippines, China: add 8^h (no DST)
Japan, Korea: add 9^h (no DST)

Australia/New Zealand

Western Australia: + 8^h (no DST)
Northern Territory: + 9½^h (no DST)
South Australia: + 9½^h (to April 1 &
  from Oct 1, + 10½^h for DST)
Queensland: + 10^h (no DST)
ACT, NSW, Victoria, Tasmania: + 10^h (to
  Apr 1 & from Oct 1, + 11^h for DST)
New Zealand: + 12^h (to April 1 and
  from Sep 24, + 13^h for DST)

North America

Newfoundland Standard Time: − 3½^h
  (March 12 to Nov 4, − 2½^h for DST)
Atlantic Standard Time: − 4^h
  (March 12 to Nov 4, − 3^h for DST)
Eastern Standard Time: − 5^h
  (March 12 to Nov 4, − 4^h for DST)
Central Standard Time: − 6^h
  (except Saskatchewan March 12 to
  Nov 4, − 5^h for DST)
Mountain Standard Time: − 7^h (except
  AZ, March 12 to Nov 4, − 6^h for DST)
Pacific Standard Time: − 8^h
  (March 12 to Nov 4, − 7^h for DST)
Alaska Standard Time: − 9^h
  (March 12 to Nov 4, − 8^h for DST)
Hawaii Standard Time: − 10^h
  (no DST)
Mexico (mostly CST): −6^h
  (April 2 to Oct 28, −5^h for DST)

South America

Argentina: −3^h (no DST)
Brazil (Eastern): −3^h (DST to Feb 18
  and from Oct 15, −2^h)
Chile: −4^h (DST to May 13 and from
  Aug 13, −3^h)
Columbia, Peru: −5^h (no DST)

All times in GMT

Date	Const. of Moon	Solar & lunar aspects	Moon Trines	El'ment	Parts of the plant enhanced by Moon or planets	Weather

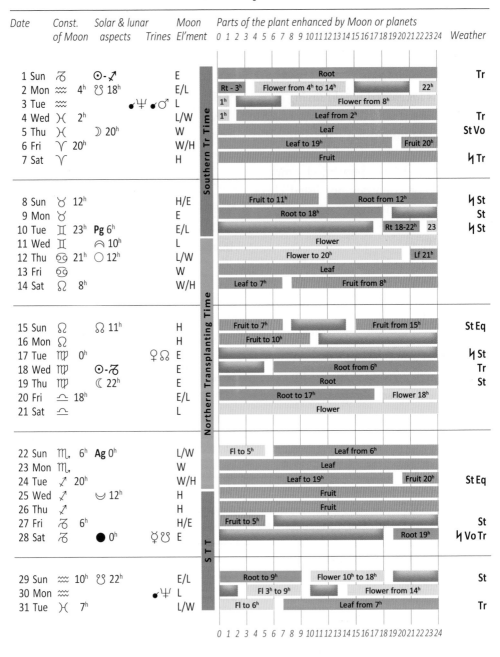

0 1 2 3 4 5 6 7 8 9 10 11 12 13 14 15 16 17 18 19 20 21 22 23 24

Southern Tr Time

1 Sun ♑ ☉-♐ — E — Root — Tr
2 Mon ♒ 4ʰ ☊ 18ʰ — E/L — Rt - 3ʰ / Flower from 4ʰ to 14ʰ / 22ʰ —
3 Tue ♒ — ♦♆ ♂♂ — L — 1ʰ / Flower from 8ʰ —
4 Wed ♓ 2ʰ — L/W — 1ʰ / Leaf from 2ʰ — Tr
5 Thu ♓ ☽ 20ʰ — W — Leaf — St Vo
6 Fri ♈ 20ʰ — W/H — Leaf to 19ʰ / Fruit 20ʰ —
7 Sat ♈ — H — Fruit — ♄ Tr

Northern Transplanting Time

8 Sun ♉ 12ʰ — H/E — Fruit to 11ʰ / Root from 12ʰ — ♄ St
9 Mon ♉ — E — Root to 18ʰ — St
10 Tue ♊ 23ʰ **Pg** 6ʰ — E/L — Rt 18-22ʰ / 23 — ♄ St
11 Wed ♊ ♒ 10ʰ — L — Flower —
12 Thu ♋ 21ʰ ○ 12ʰ — L/W — Flower to 20ʰ / Lf 21ʰ —
13 Fri ♋ — W — Leaf —
14 Sat ♌ 8ʰ — W/H — Leaf to 7ʰ / Fruit from 8ʰ —

15 Sun ♌ ♌ 11ʰ — H — Fruit to 7ʰ / Fruit from 15ʰ — St Eq
16 Mon ♌ — H — Fruit to 10ʰ —
17 Tue ♍ 0ʰ ♀♌ — E — Root from 6ʰ — ♄ St
18 Wed ♍ ☉-♑ — E — Root from 6ʰ — Tr
19 Thu ♍ ☽ 22ʰ — E — Root — St
20 Fri ♎ 18ʰ — E/L — Root to 17ʰ / Flower 18ʰ —
21 Sat ♎ — L — Flower —

STT

22 Sun ♏ 6ʰ **Ag** 0ʰ — L/W — Fl to 5ʰ / Leaf from 6ʰ —
23 Mon ♏ — W — Leaf —
24 Tue ♐ 20ʰ — W/H — Leaf to 19ʰ / Fruit 20ʰ — St Eq
25 Wed ♐ ☽ 12ʰ — H — Fruit —
26 Thu ♐ — H — Fruit —
27 Fri ♑ 6ʰ — H/E — Fruit to 5ʰ — St
28 Sat ♑ ● 0ʰ ♀☊ — E — Root 19ʰ — ♄ Vo Tr

29 Sun ♒ 10ʰ ☊ 22ʰ — E/L — Root to 9ʰ / Flower 10ʰ to 18ʰ — St
30 Mon ♒ ♦♆ — L — Fl 3ʰ to 9ʰ / Flower from 14ʰ —
31 Tue ♓ 7ʰ — L/W — Fl to 6ʰ / Leaf from 7ʰ — Tr

0 1 2 3 4 5 6 7 8 9 10 11 12 13 14 15 16 17 18 19 20 21 22 23 24

Mercury ☿	Venus ♀	Mars ♂	Jupiter ♃	Saturn ♄	Uranus ♅	Neptune ♆	Pluto ♇
♐	♒	♒	♍	♏	♓	♒	♐
(R 8 D)	24 ♓	17 ♓					

NB: All zodiac symbols refer to astronomical constellations, not astrological signs (see p. 24)

Planetary aspects
*(**Bold** = visible to naked eye)*

January 2017

1 ♂☌♆ 7ʰ
2 ☽☌♀ 8ʰ
3 ☽⚹♆ 4ʰ ☽⚹♂ 7ʰ
4
5
6 ☽☌☋ 4ʰ ☽☍♃ 6ʰ
7 ☉☌♇ 7ʰ

8
9
10 ☽☍♄ 11ʰ ☽☍☿ 22ʰ
11
12 ☽☍♇ 3ʰ ♀☌♆ 22ʰ
13
14

15 ☾☍♆ 22ʰ
16 ☾☍♀ 4ʰ ☾☍♂ 19ʰ
17 ♀☊ 18ʰ
18
19 ☾☍☋ 4ʰ ☾☌♃ 7ʰ
20
21

22
23
24 ☾☌♄ 11ʰ
25
26 ☾☌☿ 0ʰ ☾☌♇ 9ʰ
27
28 ☿☋ 6ʰ

29 ☿☌♇ 20ʰ
30 ☽⚹♆ 11ʰ
31 ☽☌♀ 18ʰ

At the beginning of the month Mercury, Venus and Mars, supported by Neptune and Pluto, will bring warmth and light. From Jan 17 Water and cool Earth influences will try to work against Mercury bringing cool precipitation.

Northern Transplanting Time
Jan 11 12ʰ to Jan 25 10ʰ
Southern Transplanting Time
Dec 29 to Jan 11 7ʰ and
Jan 25 14ʰ to Feb 7

The transplanting time is a good time for **pruning fruit trees, vines and hedges.** Fruit and Flower times are preferred for this work. Avoid unfavourable times.

When **milk processing** it is best to avoid unfavourable times. This applies to both butter and cheese making. Milk which has been produced at Warmth/Fruit times yields the highest butterfat content. This is also the case on days with a tendency for thunderstorms. Times of moon perigee (**Pg**) are almost always unfavourable for milk processing and even yoghurt will not turn out well. Starter cultures from such days decay rapidly and it is advisable to produce double the amount the day before. Milk loves Light and Warmth times best of all. Water times are unsuitable.

Southern hemisphere harvest time for seeds
Fruit seeds: Jan 14 8ʰ to Jan 16 10ʰ and at other Fruit times, always avoiding unfavourable times.
Flower seeds: Flower times.
Leaf seeds: Leaf times.
Root seeds: Root times.

Control slugs from Jan 12 21ʰ to Jan 14 7ʰ.

Planet (naked eye) visibility
Evening: Venus, Mars
All night: Jupiter
Morning: Mercury (from 4th) , Saturn

Unfavourable time

February 2017

All times in GMT

Date	Const. of Moon	Solar & lunar aspects	Moon Trines	El'ment	Parts of the plant enhanced by Moon or planets	Weather

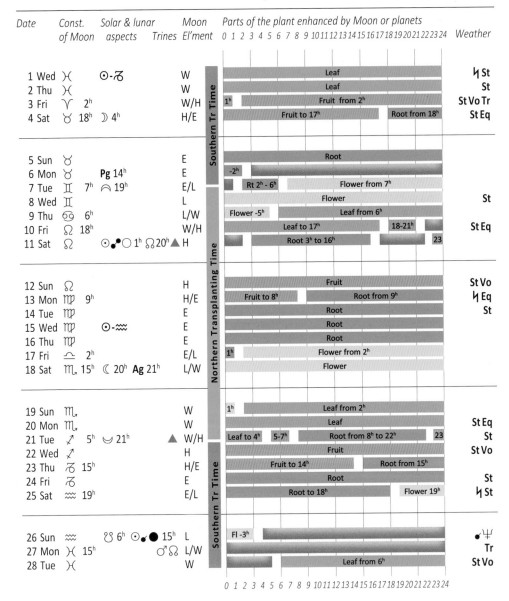

Header row for chart: Parts of the plant enhanced by Moon or planets — 0 1 2 3 4 5 6 7 8 9 10 11 12 13 14 15 16 17 18 19 20 21 22 23 24

Southern Tr Time

1 Wed	♓	☉-♑		W	Leaf	♄ St
2 Thu	♓			W	Leaf	St
3 Fri	♈	2ʰ		W/H	1ʰ Fruit from 2ʰ	St Vo Tr
4 Sat	♉ 18ʰ	☽ 4ʰ		H/E	Fruit to 17ʰ — Root from 18ʰ	St Eq

5 Sun	♉			E	Root	
6 Mon	♉	Pg 14ʰ		E	-2ʰ	
7 Tue	♊ 7ʰ	♋ 19ʰ		E/L	Rt 2ʰ - 6ʰ — Flower from 7ʰ	
8 Wed	♊			L	Flower	St
9 Thu	♋ 6ʰ			L/W	Flower -5ʰ — Leaf from 6ʰ	
10 Fri	♌ 18ʰ			W/H	Leaf to 17ʰ — 18-21ʰ	St Eq
11 Sat	♌	☉•☌○ 1ʰ ♌20ʰ ▲		H	Root 3ʰ to 16ʰ — 23	

Northern Transplanting Time

12 Sun	♌			H	Fruit	St Vo
13 Mon	♍ 9ʰ			H/E	Fruit to 8ʰ — Root from 9ʰ	♄ Eq
14 Tue	♍			E	Root	St
15 Wed	♍	☉-♒		E	Root	
16 Thu	♍			E	Root	
17 Fri	♎ 2ʰ			E/L	1ʰ Flower from 2ʰ	
18 Sat	♏ 15ʰ	☾ 20ʰ Ag 21ʰ		L/W	Flower	

Southern Tr Time

19 Sun	♏			W	1ʰ Leaf from 2ʰ	
20 Mon	♏			W	Leaf	St Eq
21 Tue	♐ 5ʰ	☽ 21ʰ	▲	W/H	Leaf to 4ʰ — 5-7ʰ — Root from 8ʰ to 22ʰ — 23	St
22 Wed	♐			H	Fruit	St Vo
23 Thu	♑ 15ʰ			H/E	Fruit to 14ʰ — Root from 15ʰ	
24 Fri	♑			E	Root	St
25 Sat	♒ 19ʰ			E/L	Root to 18ʰ — Flower 19ʰ	♄ St

26 Sun	♒	☍ 6ʰ ☉•● 15ʰ		L	Fl -3ʰ	♇ ♆
27 Mon	♓ 15ʰ	♂♌		L/W		Tr
28 Tue	♓			W	Leaf from 6ʰ	St Vo

0 1 2 3 4 5 6 7 8 9 10 11 12 13 14 15 16 17 18 19 20 21 22 23 24

Mercury ☿	Venus ♀	Mars ♂	Jupiter ♃	Saturn ♄	Uranus ♅	Neptune ♆	Pluto ♇
♐ 6 ♑	♓	♓	♍	♏	♓	♒	♐
24 ♒			(6 R)				

34   *NB: All zodiac symbols refer to astronomical constellations, not astrological signs (see p. 24)*

Planetary aspects
(**Bold** = *visible to naked eye*)

1 ☽☌♂ 3ʰ
2 ☽☌♁ 11ʰ ☽☍♃ 14ʰ
3
4

5
6 ☽☍♄ 23ʰ
7
8 ☽☍♇ 14ʰ
9 ☽☍☿ 15ʰ
10
11 ☉△♃ 15ʰ

12 ☾☌♆ 10ʰ
13
14 ☾☍♀ 11ʰ ☾☍♂ 22ʰ
15 ☾☍♁ 14ʰ ☾☌♃ 17ʰ
16
17
18

19
20
21 ☾☌♄ 0ʰ ☿△♃ 18ʰ
22 ☾☌♇ 20ʰ
23
24
25

26 ☾☌☿ 1ʰ ☽♆ 21ʰ
27 ♂☌♁ 0ʰ ♂☊ 6ʰ ♂☍♃ 14ʰ
28

In the first week Mercury is still in the warm constellation of Sagittarius, but then moves to cool Capricorn. Supported by Jupiter in Virgo, this could bring some cold against the predominant Water influences.

Northern Transplanting Time
Feb 7 21ʰ to Feb 21 19ʰ
Southern Transplanting Time
Jan 25 to Feb 7 17ʰ and
Feb 21 23ʰ to March 6

Vines, fruit trees and shrubs can be pruned during Transplanting Time selecting Flower and Fruit times in preference. Avoid unfavourable times.

Best times for taking **willow cuttings for hedges and fences:** At Flower times outside Transplanting Time. In warm areas at Flower times during Transplanting Time to avoid too strong a sap current.

Southern hemisphere harvest time for seeds
Fruit seeds: Feb 10 18ʰ to 21ʰ, and Feb 11 23ʰ to Feb 13 8ʰ and at other Fruit times.
Flower seeds: Feb 7 7ʰ to Feb 9 5ʰ and at other Flower times.

Control slugs from Feb 9 6ʰ to Feb 10 17ʰ.

Planet (naked eye) visibility
Evening: Venus, Mars
All night: Jupiter
Morning: Mercury (to 2nd) , Saturn

Unfavourable time 35

March 2017

Date	Const. of Moon	Solar & lunar aspects	Moon Trines	El'ment	Parts of the plant enhanced by Moon or planets	Weather
1 Wed	♓	☉-≈		W	Leaf	♄ St
2 Thu	♈	8ʰ		W/H	Leaf to 7ʰ; Fruit from 8ʰ to 20ʰ	St Vo
3 Fri	♈	Pg 7ʰ		H	20-23ʰ	
4 Sat	♉	0ʰ		E	Root from 0ʰ	Tr
5 Sun	♉	☽ 12ʰ	▲	E	Root to 8ʰ; Leaf from 9ʰ	St Eq
6 Mon	♊	13ʰ		E/L	1ʰ Root from 2ʰ to 12ʰ; Flower from 13ʰ	♄ St
7 Tue	♊	⌢ 1ʰ		L	Flower	
8 Wed	♋	13ʰ		L/W	Flower to 12ʰ; Leaf from 13ʰ	
9 Thu	♋			W	Leaf	
10 Fri	♌	2ʰ		W/H	1ʰ Fruit from 2ʰ	
11 Sat	♌	⧎ 4ʰ		H	1ʰ Fruit from 9ʰ	St
12 Sun	♍	18ʰ ☉-♓ ○15ʰ		H/E	Fruit to 17ʰ; Root from 18ʰ	St
13 Mon	♍			E	Root	
14 Tue	♍			E	Root	Vo Tr
15 Wed	♍			E	Root	
16 Thu	♎	11ʰ		E/L	Root to 10ʰ; Flower from 11ʰ	
17 Fri	♏	23ʰ		L/W	Flower to 22ʰ	St
18 Sat	♏	Ag 17ʰ	☿♌	W		
19 Sun	♏			W	Leaf from 12ʰ	
20 Mon	♐	13ʰ ☾16ʰ		W/H	Leaf to 12ʰ; Fruit from 13ʰ	
21 Tue	♐	⌣ 5ʰ		H	Fruit	Vo Tr
22 Wed	♐			H	Fruit to 23ʰ	
23 Thu	♑	0ʰ		E	Root from 0ʰ	St Eq
24 Fri	♑			E	Root	St Vo
25 Sat	≈	4ʰ ⧎16ʰ		E/L	Rt -3ʰ; Flower 4ʰ to 12ʰ; Flower 19ʰ	St
26 Sun	≈	•♆		L	Flower to 6ʰ; Flower from 11ʰ to 23ʰ	
27 Mon	♓	0ʰ		W	Leaf from 0ʰ	St
28 Tue	♓	● 3ʰ		W	Leaf	
29 Wed	♈	16ʰ	▲	W/H	Leaf to 21ʰ; 22ʰ	St Eq
30 Thu	♈	Pg 12ʰ		H	1ʰ	St Vo
31 Fri	♉	7ʰ		H/E	Fr 2ʰ - 6ʰ; Root from 7ʰ	Vo Tr

Southern Tr Time — Northern Transplanting Time — Southern Transplanting Time

DST begins in North America (12 Sun)

DST begins in Europe (incl UK). All times below continue in GMT (26 Sun)

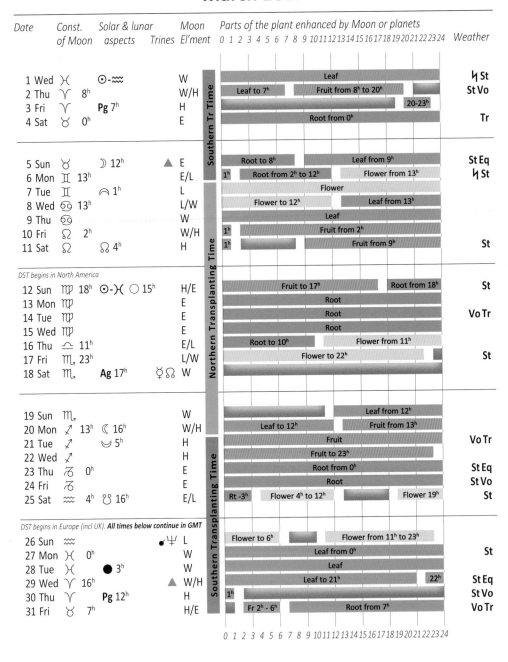

0 1 2 3 4 5 6 7 8 9 10 11 12 13 14 15 16 17 18 19 20 21 22 23 24

Mercury ☿	Venus ♀	Mars ♂	Jupiter ♃	Saturn ♄	Uranus ♅	Neptune ♆	Pluto ♇
≈ 9 ♓	♓	♓	♍	♏	♓	≈	♐
31 ♈	(4 R)	9 ♈	(R)				

NB: All zodiac symbols refer to astronomical constellations, not astrological signs (see p. 24)

Planetary aspects
*(**Bold** = visible to naked eye)*

March 2017

Day	Aspects
1	**☽☌♀** 3^h ☽☌⊕ 18^h **☽☍♃** 19^h **☽☌♂** 22^h
2	☉☌♆ 3^h
3	♃☍⊕ 2^h
4	☿☌♆ 11^h
5	♂△♄ 21^h
6	☽☍♄ 8^h
7	☉☌☿ 1^h ☽☍♇ 21^h
8	
9	
10	
11	☽☍♆ 20^h
12	
13	☾☍☿ 3^h
14	☾☍♀ 4^h ☾☌♃ 22^h
15	☾☍⊕ 1^h
16	☾☍♂ 0^h
17	
18	☿☌♀ 12^h ☿☌☊ 22^h
19	
20	☾☌♄ 11^h
21	
22	☾☌♇ 6^h
23	
24	☿☍♃ 13^h
25	☉☌♀ 10^h
26	☾☌♆ 8^h ☿☌⊕ 15^h
27	☾☌♀ 20^h
28	☽☍♃ 23^h
29	☽☌⊕ 5^h ☽☌☿ 12^h ☿△♄ 18^h
30	☽☌♂ 16^h
31	

Will Mercury bring some warmth and light in the first week? From March 9 there will be much precipitation. Will Jupiter retrograde in Virgo bring some wintry cold?

Northern Transplanting Time
March 7 3^h to March 21 4^h
Southern Transplanting Time
Feb 21 to March 6 23^h and
March 21 8^h to April 3

Willow cuttings for **pollen production** are best cut from March 16 11^h to March 17 22^h; and for **honey flow** from March 10 2^h to March 12 17^h. Avoid unfavourable times.

The cuttings taken in February are best stuck in the ground during transplanting time; to improve pollen production do this at Flower times, and to increase honey flow do this at Fruit times.

Control slugs from March 8 13^h to March 10 1^h.

Cuttings for grafting: Cut outside Transplanting Time during ascending Moon – always choosing times (Fruit, Leaf, etc.) according to the part of plant to be enhanced.

Southern hemisphere harvest time for seeds
Fruit seeds: March 10 2^h to March 12 17^h and at other Fruit times.
Flower seeds: March 6 13^h to March 8 12^h and at other Flower times.
Leaf seeds: March 8 13^h to March 10 1^h and at other Leaf times.
Root seeds: Root times.
Always avoid unfavourable times.

Biodynamic preparations: Pick dandelion in March or April in the mornings during Flower times. The flowers should not be quite open in the centre. Dry them on paper in the shade, not in bright sunlight.

Planet (naked eye) visibility
Evening: Mercury (from 18th), Venus (to 23rd), Mars
All night: Jupiter
Morning: Venus (from 21st), Saturn

▬▬▬ *Unfavourable time*

April 2017

All times in GMT

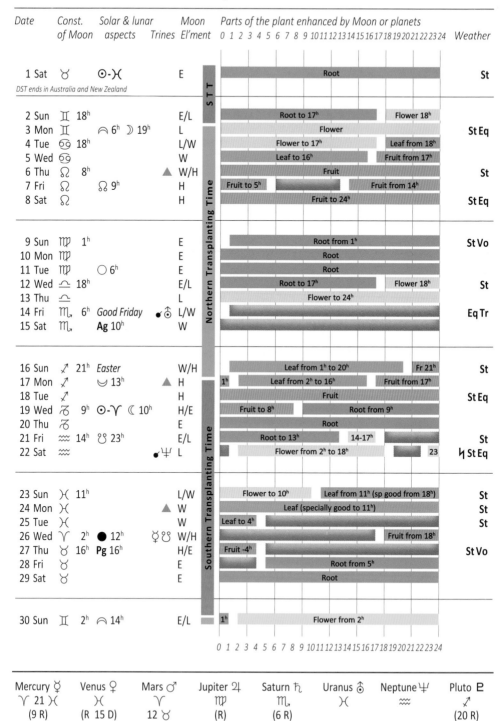

Date	Const. of Moon	Solar & lunar aspects	Moon Trines El'ment	Parts of the plant enhanced by Moon or planets (0–24)	Weather
1 Sat	♉	☉-)(	E	Root	St

DST ends in Australia and New Zealand

Date	Const. of Moon	Solar & lunar aspects	Moon Trines El'ment	Parts of the plant enhanced by Moon or planets	Weather
2 Sun	♊ 18h		E/L	Root to 17h — Flower 18h	
3 Mon	♊	♎ 6h ☽ 19h	L	Flower	St Eq
4 Tue	♋ 18h		L/W	Flower to 17h — Leaf from 18h	
5 Wed	♋		W	Leaf to 16h — Fruit from 17h	
6 Thu	♌ 8h	▲	W/H	Fruit	St
7 Fri	♌	☍ 9h	H	Fruit to 5h — Fruit from 14h	
8 Sat	♌		H	Fruit to 24h	St Eq
9 Sun	♍ 1h		E	Root from 1h	St Vo
10 Mon	♍		E	Root	
11 Tue	♍	○ 6h	E	Root	
12 Wed	♎ 18h		E/L	Root to 17h — Flower 18h	St
13 Thu	♎		L	Flower to 24h	
14 Fri	♏ 6h *Good Friday*	●☊	L/W		Eq Tr
15 Sat	♏	**Ag 10h**	W		
16 Sun	♐ 21h *Easter*		W/H	Leaf from 1h to 20h — Fr 21h	St
17 Mon	♐	☽ 13h	▲ H	1h — Leaf from 2h to 16h — Fruit from 17h	
18 Tue	♐		H	Fruit	St Eq
19 Wed	♑ 9h	☉-♈ ☾ 10h	H/E	Fruit to 8h — Root from 9h	
20 Thu	♑		E	Root	
21 Fri	♒ 14h	☊ 23h	E/L	Root to 13h — 14–17h	St
22 Sat	♒	●♆	L	Flower from 2h to 18h — 23	♄ St Eq
23 Sun	)(11h		L/W	Flower to 10h — Leaf from 11h (sp good from 18h)	St
24 Mon	)(	▲	W	Leaf (specially good to 11h)	St
25 Tue	)(		W	Leaf to 4h	St
26 Wed	♈ 2h	● 12h ☿☊	W/H	Fruit from 18h	St Vo
27 Thu	♉ 16h	**Pg 16h**	H/E	Fruit -4h	
28 Fri	♉		E	Root from 5h	
29 Sat	♉		E	Root	
30 Sun	♊ 2h	♎ 14h	E/L	1h — Flower from 2h	

STT

Northern Transplanting Time

Southern Transplanting Time

In UK/Ireland remember to add 1 hour for Daylight Saving Time

Mercury ☿	Venus ♀	Mars ♂	Jupiter ♃	Saturn ♄	Uranus ♅	Neptune ♆	Pluto ♇
♈ 21)(	)(	♈	♍	♏	)(	♒	♐
(9 R)	(R 15 D)	12 ♉	(R)	(6 R)			(20 R)

NB: All zodiac symbols refer to astronomical constellations, not astrological signs (see p. 24)

Planetary aspects
    (**Bold** = visible to naked eye)

April 2017

1 _____

2 ☽☌♄ 15h _____

3 _____

4 ☽☍♇ 4h _____

5 _____

6 ♂△♇ 4h _____

7 ☉☍♃ 22h _____

8 ☽☍♆ 5h _____

9 ☽☍♀ 8h _____

10 ☽☌♃ 23h

11 ☾☌⊕ 12h

12 ☾☍☿ 8h

13 _____

14 ☾☍♂ 0h ☉●⊕ 5h

15 _____

16 ☾☌♄ 18h

17 ☉△♄ 13h

18 ☾☌♇ 14h

19 _____

20 ☉☌☿ 6h

21 _____

22 ☾●♆ 20h

23 ☾☌♀ 22h

24 ☿△♄ 6h

25 ☾☍♃ 3h ☾☌⊕ 18h ☾☌☿ 21h

26 ☿⚼ 5h

27 _____

28 ☽☌♂ 9h ☿☌⊕ 15h

29 ☽☍♄ 21h

30 _____

Mercury in Aries, initially supported by Mars, will bring warmth. When Mars moves into Taurus on April 12 cold will be added to the precipitation brought by other planets in Water constellations.

Northern Transplanting Time
April 3 8h to April 17 11h and
April 30 16h to May 14
Southern Transplanting Time
March 21 to April 3 4h and
April 17 15h to April 30 12h

The **soil warms up** on April 1.

Grafting of fruiting shrubs at Fruit times outside transplanting times.
    Grafting of flowering shrubs at Flower times outside transplanting times.

Control
Slugs from April 4 18h to April 5 16h.
Moths from April 23 11h to April 25 4h.
Clothes and wax moths from April 26 18h to April 27 4h.

Southern hemisphere harvest time for seeds
Fruit seeds: April 5 17h to April 8 24h and at other Fruit times.
Flower seeds at Flower times, **Leaf seeds** at Leaf times, and **Root seeds** at Root times, always avoiding unfavourable times.

Biodynamic preparations: The preparations can be taken out of the earth, avoiding unfavourable times.

Planet (naked eye) visibility
Evening: Mercury (to 13th), Mars
All night: Jupiter, Saturn
Morning: Venus

Unfavourable time

May 2017

Date	Const. of Moon	Solar & lunar aspects	Moon Trines	El'ment	Parts of the plant enhanced by Moon or planets	Weather

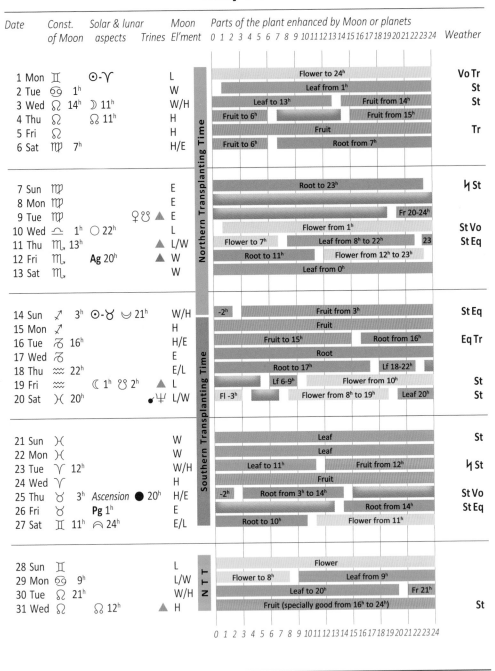

Northern Transplanting Time

- 1 Mon ♊ — ☉-♈ — L — Flower to 24ʰ — Vo Tr
- 2 Tue ♋ 1ʰ — W — Leaf from 1ʰ — St
- 3 Wed ♌ 14ʰ ☽ 11ʰ — W/H — Leaf to 13ʰ · Fruit from 14ʰ — St
- 4 Thu ♌ ☍ 11ʰ — H — Fruit to 6ʰ · Fruit from 15ʰ
- 5 Fri ♌ — H — Fruit — Tr
- 6 Sat ♍ 7ʰ — H/E — Fruit to 6ʰ · Root from 7ʰ

- 7 Sun ♍ — E — Root to 23ʰ — ♄ St
- 8 Mon ♍ — E —
- 9 Tue ♍ ♀☍ ▲ — E — Fr 20-24ʰ
- 10 Wed ♎ 1ʰ ○ 22ʰ — L — Flower from 1ʰ — St Vo
- 11 Thu ♏ 13ʰ ▲ L/W — Flower to 7ʰ · Leaf from 8ʰ to 22ʰ · 23 — St Eq
- 12 Fri ♏ Ag 20ʰ ▲ W — Root to 11ʰ · Flower from 12ʰ to 23ʰ
- 13 Sat ♏ — W — Leaf from 0ʰ

Southern Transplanting Time

- 14 Sun ♐ 3ʰ ☉-♉ ☋ 21ʰ — W/H — -2ʰ · Fruit from 3ʰ — St Eq
- 15 Mon ♐ — H — Fruit
- 16 Tue ♑ 16ʰ — H/E — Fruit to 15ʰ · Root from 16ʰ — Eq Tr
- 17 Wed ♑ — E — Root
- 18 Thu ♒ 22ʰ — E/L — Root to 17ʰ · Lf 18-22ʰ
- 19 Fri ♒ ☾ 1ʰ ☋ 2ʰ ▲ L — Lf 6-9ʰ · Flower from 10ʰ — St
- 20 Sat ♓ 20ʰ •♆ L/W — Fl -3ʰ · Flower from 8ʰ to 19ʰ · Leaf 20ʰ — St

- 21 Sun ♓ — W — Leaf — St
- 22 Mon ♓ — W — Leaf
- 23 Tue ♈ 12ʰ — W/H — Leaf to 11ʰ · Fruit from 12ʰ — ♄ St
- 24 Wed ♈ — H — Fruit
- 25 Thu ♉ 3ʰ Ascension ● 20ʰ — H/E — -2ʰ · Root from 3ʰ to 14ʰ — St Vo
- 26 Fri ♉ Pg 1ʰ — E — Root from 14ʰ — St Eq
- 27 Sat ♊ 11ʰ ⌒ 24ʰ — E/L — Root to 10ʰ · Flower from 11ʰ

NTT

- 28 Sun ♊ — L — Flower
- 29 Mon ♋ 9ʰ — L/W — Flower to 8ʰ · Leaf from 9ʰ
- 30 Tue ♌ 21ʰ — W/H — Leaf to 20ʰ · Fr 21ʰ
- 31 Wed ♌ ☍ 12ʰ ▲ H — Fruit (specially good from 16ʰ to 24ʰ) — St

Mercury ☿	Venus ♀	Mars ♂	Jupiter ♃	Saturn ♄	Uranus ♅	Neptune ♆	Pluto ♇
♓ 15 ♈	♓	♉	♍	♏	♓	♒	♐
(R 3 D)			(R)	(R)			(R)

40   *NB: All zodiac symbols refer to astronomical constellations, not astrological signs (see p. 24)*

Planetary aspects
    (**Bold** = *visible to naked eye*)

1	☽☌♇ 10ʰ
2	
3	
4	
5	☽☌♆ 11ʰ
6	
7	☽☍♀ 3ʰ ☽☌♃ 23ʰ
8	☽☍♀ 20ʰ ☽☍♁ 21ʰ
9	♀☋ 7ʰ ☉△♇ 18ʰ
10	☿☌♁ 5ʰ
11	☿△♄ 20ʰ
12	♂△♃ 10ʰ ☾☍♂ 23ʰ
13	☾☌♄ 23ʰ
14	
15	☾☌♇ 20ʰ
16	
17	
18	
19	♄△♁ 7ʰ ♀☍♃ 14ʰ
20	☾●♆ 6ʰ
21	
22	☾☍♃ 10ʰ ☾☌♀ 14ʰ
23	☾☌♁ 7ʰ
24	☾☌☿ 2ʰ
25	
26	
27	☽☌♂ 2ʰ ☽☍♄ 5ʰ
28	☽☍♇ 18ʰ
29	♂☍♄ 7ʰ
30	
31	☿△♇ 12ʰ

Planet (naked eye) visibility
Evening: Mars (to 22nd)
All night: Jupiter, Saturn
Morning: Venus

May is similar to April. Mercury is in Pisces, leaving this watery region on May 15 to Aries. In contrast to this Warmth influence, Mars in Taurus brings an underlying coolness.

Northern Transplanting Time
April 30 to May 14 19ʰ and
May 28 2ʰ to June 11
Southern Transplanting Time
May 14 23ʰ to May 27 22ʰ

Transplant **table potatoes** at Root times. Transplant **seed potatoes** for 2018 from May 23 12ʰ to May 25 2ʰ.

Hay should be cut between May 27 11ʰ and May 29 8ʰ, and at other Flower times.

Control:
Flies by burning fly papers in the cow barn at Flower times.
Chitinous insects, wheat weevil, Colorado beetle and varroa from May 25 3ʰ to May 27 10ʰ.

Begin **queen bee** rearing (grafting or larval transfer, comb insertion, cell punching) at Flower times, especially when Moon is in Gemini (April 30 2ʰ to May 1 24ʰ, and May 27 11ʰ to May 29 8ʰ).

Biodynamic preparations: Cut birch, fill with yarrow and hang on May 19, 10ʰ to 18ʰ.

June 2017

Date	Const. of Moon	Solar & lunar aspects	Moon Trines El'ment	Parts of the plant enhanced by Moon or planets 0 1 2 3 4 5 6 7 8 9 10 11 12 13 14 15 16 17 18 19 20 21 22 23 24	Weather

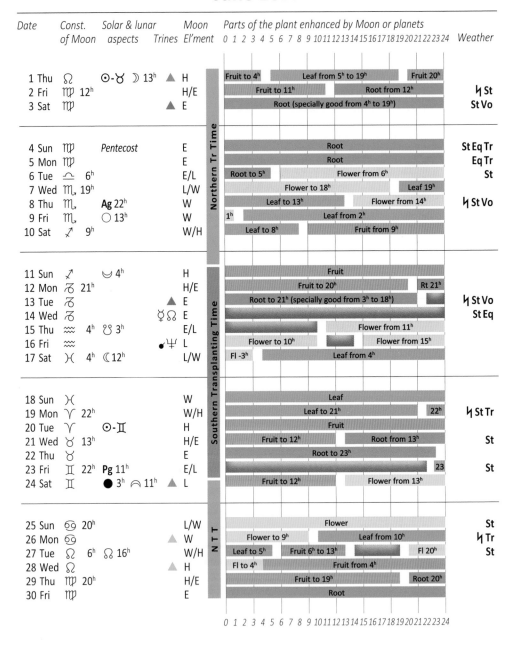

Table content (left labels and data):

1 Thu ♌ ⊙-♉ ☽ 13ʰ ▲ H — Fruit to 4ʰ / Leaf from 5ʰ to 19ʰ / Fruit 20ʰ
2 Fri ♍ 12ʰ H/E — Fruit to 11ʰ / Root from 12ʰ — ♄ St
3 Sat ♍ ▲ E — Root (specially good from 4ʰ to 19ʰ) — St Vo

Northern Tr Time

4 Sun ♍ Pentecost E — Root — St Eq Tr
5 Mon ♍ E — Root — Eq Tr
6 Tue ♎ 6ʰ E/L — Root to 5ʰ / Flower from 6ʰ — St
7 Wed ♏ 19ʰ L/W — Flower to 18ʰ / Leaf 19ʰ
8 Thu ♏ Ag 22ʰ W — Leaf to 13ʰ / Flower from 14ʰ — ♄ St Vo
9 Fri ♏ ○ 13ʰ W — 1ʰ / Leaf from 2ʰ
10 Sat ♐ 9ʰ W/H — Leaf to 8ʰ / Fruit from 9ʰ

Southern Transplanting Time

11 Sun ♐ ☽ 4ʰ H — Fruit
12 Mon ♑ 21ʰ H/E — Fruit to 20ʰ / Rt 21ʰ
13 Tue ♑ ▲ E — Root to 21ʰ (specially good from 3ʰ to 18ʰ) — ♄ St Vo
14 Wed ♑ ☿♌ E — St Eq
15 Thu ♒ 4ʰ ☍ 3ʰ E/L — Flower from 11ʰ
16 Fri ♒ ●♆ L — Flower to 10ʰ / Flower from 15ʰ
17 Sat ♓ 4ʰ ☾ 12ʰ L/W — Fl -3ʰ / Leaf from 4ʰ

18 Sun ♓ W — Leaf
19 Mon ♈ 22ʰ W/H — Leaf to 21ʰ / 22ʰ — ♄ St Tr
20 Tue ♈ ⊙-♊ H — Fruit
21 Wed ♉ 13ʰ H/E — Fruit to 12ʰ / Root from 13ʰ — St
22 Thu ♉ E — Root to 23ʰ
23 Fri ♊ 22ʰ Pg 11ʰ E/L — 23 — St
24 Sat ♊ ● 3ʰ ⌒ 11ʰ ▲ L — Fruit to 12ʰ / Flower from 13ʰ

NTT

25 Sun ♋ 20ʰ L/W — Flower — St
26 Mon ♋ ▲ W — Flower to 9ʰ / Leaf from 10ʰ — ♄ Tr
27 Tue ♌ 6ʰ ☍ 16ʰ W/H — Leaf to 5ʰ / Fruit 6ʰ to 13ʰ / Fl 20ʰ — St
28 Wed ♌ ▲ H — Fl to 4ʰ / Fruit from 4ʰ
29 Thu ♍ 20ʰ H/E — Fruit to 19ʰ / Root 20ʰ
30 Fri ♍ E — Root

0 1 2 3 4 5 6 7 8 9 10 11 12 13 14 15 16 17 18 19 20 21 22 23 24

Mercury ☿	Venus ♀	Mars ♂	Jupiter ♃	Saturn ♄	Uranus ⛢	Neptune ♆	Pluto ♇
♈ 3 ♉	♓ 6 ♈	♉	♍	♏	♓	♒	♐
21 ♊	29 ♉	4 ♊	(R 9 D)	(R)		(16 R)	(R)

NB: All zodiac symbols refer to astronomical constellations, not astrological signs (see p. 24)

Planetary aspects

(**Bold** = *visible to naked eye)*

1 **♀△♄** 15^h ☽☍♆ 18^h
2
3 ♀☌⛢ 8^h ☉△♃ 16^h
4 **☽☌♃** 2^h
5 ☽☍⛢ 5^h ☽☍♀ 9^h
6
7
8 ☽☍☿ 4^h
9
10 **☾☌♄** 1^h ☾☍♂ 20^h
11
12 ☾☌♇ 1^h
13 ☿△♃ 16^h
14 ☿☊ 21^h
15 ☉☍♄ 10^h
16 ☾●♆ 13^h
17
18 ☾☍♃ 17^h ☿☍♄ 19^h
19 ☾☌⛢ 18^h
20 **☾☌♀** 22^h
21 ☉☌☿ 14^h
22
23 ☾☍♄ 13^h
24 ☽☌☿ 8^h ♀△♇ 9^h ☽☌♂ 19^h
25 ☽☍♇ 4^h
26 ♂△♆ 7^h
27
28 ☿△♆ 0^h ☿☌♂ 20^h
29 ☽☍♆ 2^h
30 ☿☍♇ 1^h

Planet (naked eye) visibility
Evening:
All night: Jupiter, Saturn
Morning: Venus

June 2017

The first few days of June will be similar to May. Then Mercury will bring cool influences from Taurus, while Venus, in Aries continues to bring Warmth. Mars in Gemini brings light influence, perhaps leading bees to make honeydew honey. Neither in May nor in June does Venus bring any Light infuence to enhance hay quality.

Northern Transplanting Time
May 28 to June 11 2^h and
June 24 13^h to July 8
Southern Transplanting Time
June 11 6^h to June 24 9^h

Cut **hay** at Flower times.

Begin **queen bee** rearing June 15 11^h to June 17 3^h and at other Flower times, avoiding unfavourable times.

Control:
Flies by burning fly papers in the cow barn at Flower times.
Mole crickets ash from June 7 19^h to June 10 8^h.
Grasshoppers from June 23 22^h to June 25 19^h.

June

Unfavourable time

July 2017

Date	Const. of Moon	Solar & lunar aspects	Trines	Moon El'ment	Parts of the plant enhanced by Moon or planets	Weather

Parts of the plant enhanced by Moon or planets — scale: 0 1 2 3 4 5 6 7 8 9 10 11 12 13 14 15 16 17 18 19 20 21 22 23 24

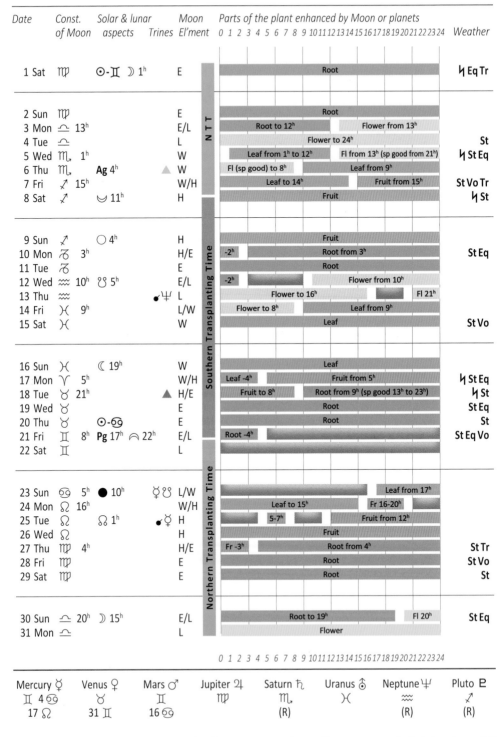

N T T

- 1 Sat ♍ ☉-♊ ☽ 1ʰ — E — Root — ♄ Eq Tr

- 2 Sun ♍ — E — Root
- 3 Mon ♎ 13ʰ — E/L — Root to 12ʰ / Flower from 13ʰ
- 4 Tue ♎ — L — Flower to 24ʰ — St
- 5 Wed ♏ 1ʰ — W — Leaf from 1ʰ to 12ʰ / Fl from 13ʰ (sp good from 21ʰ) — ♄ St Eq
- 6 Thu ♏ Ag 4ʰ ▲ — W — Fl (sp good) to 8ʰ / Leaf from 9ʰ
- 7 Fri ♐ 15ʰ — W/H — Leaf to 14ʰ / Fruit from 15ʰ — St Vo Tr
- 8 Sat ♐ ☋ 11ʰ — H — Fruit — ♄ St

Southern Transplanting Time

- 9 Sun ♐ ○ 4ʰ — H — Fruit
- 10 Mon ♑ 3ʰ — H/E — -2ʰ / Root from 3ʰ — St Eq
- 11 Tue ♑ — E — Root
- 12 Wed ♒ 10ʰ ☊ 5ʰ — E/L — -2ʰ / Flower from 10ʰ
- 13 Thu ♒ •♆ — L — Flower to 16ʰ / Fl 21ʰ
- 14 Fri ♓ 9ʰ — L/W — Flower to 8ʰ / Leaf from 9ʰ
- 15 Sat ♓ — W — Leaf — St Vo

- 16 Sun ♓ ☾ 19ʰ — W — Leaf
- 17 Mon ♈ 5ʰ — W/H — Leaf -4ʰ / Fruit from 5ʰ — ♄ St Eq
- 18 Tue ♉ 21ʰ ▲ — H/E — Fruit to 8ʰ / Root from 9ʰ (sp good 13ʰ to 23ʰ) — ♄ St
- 19 Wed ♉ — E — Root — St Eq
- 20 Thu ♉ ☉-♋ — E — Root — St
- 21 Fri ♊ 8ʰ Pg 17ʰ ⌢ 22ʰ — E/L — Root -4ʰ — St Eq Vo
- 22 Sat ♊ — L

Northern Transplanting Time

- 23 Sun ♋ 5ʰ ● 10ʰ ☿ ☋ — L/W — Leaf from 17ʰ
- 24 Mon ♌ 16ʰ — W/H — Leaf to 15ʰ / Fr 16-20ʰ
- 25 Tue ♌ ☊ 1ʰ •☿ — H — 5-7ʰ / Fruit from 12ʰ
- 26 Wed ♌ — H — Fruit
- 27 Thu ♍ 4ʰ — H/E — Fr -3ʰ / Root from 4ʰ — St Tr
- 28 Fri ♍ — E — Root — St Vo
- 29 Sat ♍ — E — Root — St

- 30 Sun ♎ 20ʰ ☽ 15ʰ — E/L — Root to 19ʰ / Fl 20ʰ — St Eq
- 31 Mon ♎ — L — Flower

scale: 0 1 2 3 4 5 6 7 8 9 10 11 12 13 14 15 16 17 18 19 20 21 22 23 24

Mercury ☿	Venus ♀	Mars ♂	Jupiter ♃	Saturn ♄	Uranus ⛢	Neptune ♆	Pluto ♇
♊ 4 ♋	♉	♊	♍	♏	♓	♒	♐
17 ♌	31 ♊	16 ♋		(R)		(R)	(R)

NB: All zodiac symbols refer to astronomical constellations, not astrological signs (see p. 24)

July 2017

1	☽☌♃ 10ʰ
2	♂☌♇ 12ʰ ☽☍♄ 13ʰ
3	
4	
5	☽☍♀ 6ʰ
6	☉△♆ 1ʰ
7	☽☌♄ 4ʰ
8	
9	☾☌♇ 6ʰ ☾☍♂ 16ʰ
10	☉☍♇ 4ʰ ☾☍☿ 23ʰ
11	
12	
13	☾●♆ 18ʰ
14	
15	
16	☾☍♃ 3ʰ
17	☾☌♄ 2ʰ
18	♀△♃ 20ʰ
19	☿△♄ 19ʰ
20	☾☌♀ 12ʰ ☾☍♄ 20ʰ
21	
22	☾☍♇ 13ʰ
23	☿♊ 4ʰ ☽☌♂ 12ʰ
24	♀☍♄ 15ʰ ☿△♄ 17ʰ
25	☽●☿ 9ʰ
26	☽☍♆ 11ʰ
27	☉☌♂ 1ʰ
28	☽☌♃ 23ʰ
29	☽☍♄ 22ʰ
30	
31	

Planet (naked eye) visibility
Evening: Jupiter
All night: Saturn
Morning: Venus

The planetary influences of the first half of the year give the impression that Mercury and Venus have conspired to avoid any continuous weather influences. On July 16 Mercury moves into Leo, hopefully heralding Warmth and Fruit influences.

Northern Transplanting Time
June 24 to July 8 9ʰ and
July 22 0ʰ to Aug 4
Southern Transplanting Time
July 8 13ʰ to July 21 20ʰ

Late hay cut at Flower times.

Summer harvest for seeds:
Flower plants: Harvest at Flower times, specially in the first half of the month.
　　Fruit plants from July 24 16ʰ to July 27 3ʰ, avoiding unfavourable times, or at other Fruit times.
　　Harvest **leaf plants** at Leaf times.
　　Harvest **root plants** at Root times, especially July 18 9ʰ to July 21 4ʰ.

Control
Flies: burn fly papers in the cow barn at Flower times.
Slugs: burn between July 23 5ʰ and July 24 15ʰ. Spray leaf plants and the soil with horn silica early in the morning during Leaf times.

Biodynamic preparations
Pick **valerian** early in the morning at Flower times. Quickly press out the sap without diluting with water or laying the plants in water. Diluted sap does not keep as long. Search out valerian plants well beforehand to ensure a speedy harvest.
　　Cut **oak,** fill it with ground oak bark and put it in the earth on July 2 between 9ʰ and 16ʰ.

July

Unfavourable time

45

August 2017

Date	Const. of Moon	Solar & lunar aspects	Moon Trines	El'ment	Parts of the plant enhanced by Moon or planets 0 1 2 3 4 5 6 7 8 9 10 11 12 13 14 15 16 17 18 19 20 21 22 23 24	Weather
1 Tue	♏ 8ʰ	☉-◷		L/W	Flower to 7ʰ / Leaf from 8ʰ	St Eq
2 Wed	♏	Ag 18ʰ		W	Leaf to 8ʰ / Flower from 9ʰ to 21ʰ 22ʰ	St
3 Thu	♐ 22ʰ			W/H	Leaf to 21ʰ 22ʰ	
4 Fri	♐	☋ 18ʰ		H	Fruit	St Vo
5 Sat	♐			H	Fruit	
6 Sun	♑ 10ʰ			H/E	Fruit to 9ʰ / Root from 10ʰ	
7 Mon	♑	☉☌○ 18ʰ		E	Root to 16ʰ Rt 21ʰ	
8 Tue	♒ 16ʰ	☍ 11ʰ		E/L	Root to 6ʰ / Flower from 16ʰ	
9 Wed	♒		☌♆	L	Flower to 21ʰ	♄ Tr
10 Thu	♓ 15ʰ			L/W	Flower from 2ʰ to 14ʰ / Leaf from 15ʰ	
11 Fri	♓	☉-♌		W	Leaf to 16ʰ / Flower from 17ʰ	St Eq
12 Sat	♓		▲	W	Flower to 8ʰ / Leaf from 9ʰ	
13 Sun	♈ 10ʰ			W/H	Leaf to 9ʰ / Fruit from 10ʰ	St
14 Mon	♈			H	Fruit	
15 Tue	♉ 4ʰ	☾ 1ʰ		H/E	Fr -3ʰ / Root from 4ʰ	St Eq Vo
16 Wed	♉			E	Root	
17 Thu	♊ 16ʰ			E/L	Root to 15ʰ / Flower 16ʰ to 24ʰ	St
18 Fri	♊	⌢ 6ʰ Pg 13ʰ		L		
19 Sat	♋ 14ʰ			L/W	Flower from 1ʰ to 13ʰ / Leaf from 14ʰ	
20 Sun	♋			W	Leaf	St
21 Mon	♌ 2ʰ	☍ 11ʰ ☉☌● 18ʰ		W/H	1ʰ Fr 2ʰ - 6ʰ Fr 21ʰ	
22 Tue	♌			H	Fruit	
23 Wed	♍ 14ʰ			H/E	Fruit to 13ʰ / Root from 14ʰ	St
24 Thu	♍			E	Root	♄ St Eq
25 Fri	♍			E	Root	St Vo
26 Sat	♍			E	Root	
27 Sun	♎ 4ʰ			E/L	Rt -3ʰ / Flower from 4ʰ	
28 Mon	♏ 16ʰ			L/W	Flower to 15ʰ / Leaf from 16ʰ	St Vo
29 Tue	♏	☽ 8ʰ		W	Lf -3ʰ	St
30 Wed	♏	Ag 11ʰ	♀☍	W	Leaf	
31 Thu	♐ 6ʰ			W/H	Leaf 0ʰ - 5ʰ / Fruit from 6ʰ	St

NTT

Southern Transplanting Time

Northern Transplanting Time

0 1 2 3 4 5 6 7 8 9 10 11 12 13 14 15 16 17 18 19 20 21 22 23 24

Mercury ☿	Venus ♀	Mars ♂	Jupiter ♃	Saturn ♄	Uranus ♅	Neptune ♆	Pluto ♇
♌	♊	♋	♍	♏	♓	♒	♐
(13 R)	24 ♋	18 ♌		(R 25 D)	(3 R)	(R)	(R)

NB: All zodiac symbols refer to astronomical constellations, not astrological signs (see p. 24)

Planetary aspects
(**Bold** = *visible to naked eye*)

1

2

3 ☽ ☌ ♄ 8ʰ

4 ☽ ☍ ♀ 9ʰ

5 ☽ ☌ ♇ 12ʰ

6

7 ☽ ☍ ♂ 11ʰ

8

9 ☾ ☌ ☿ 19ʰ   ☾ • ♆ 23ʰ

10

11

12 ♀ △ ♆ 5ʰ   ☾ ☍ ♃ 15ʰ

13 ☾ ☌ ☊ 8ʰ   ☉ △ ♄ 21ʰ

14

15 ♀ ☍ ♇ 11ʰ

16

17 ☾ ☍ ♄ 2ʰ

18 ☾ ☍ ♇ 21ʰ

19 ☾ ☌ ♀ 4ʰ

20

21 ☾ ☌ ♂ 4ʰ   ☉ △ ☊ 6ʰ

22 ☽ ☌ ☿ 10ʰ   ♂ △ ♄ 13ʰ   ☽ ☍ ♆ 19ʰ

23

24

25 ☽ ☌ ♃ 16ʰ

26 ☽ ☍ ☊ 6ʰ   ☉ ☌ ☿ 21ʰ

27

28

29

30 ♀ ☊ 11ʰ   ☽ ☌ ♀ 15ʰ

31

Planet (naked eye) visibility
Evening: Jupiter
All night: Saturn
Morning: Venus

August 2017

Mercury is in Leo for the whole month, and Venus (until Aug 23) in the Light constellation of Gemini. The Sun (from Aug 11) and Mars (from Aug 18) move into Leo, hopefully bringing Warmth for a good harvest.

Northern Transplanting Time
July 22 to Aug 4 16ʰ and
Aug 18 8ʰ to Aug 31 24ʰ
Southern Transplanting Time
Aug 4 20ʰ to Aug 18 4ʰ

Harvest **seeds of fruit plants** and **grain** to be used for seed from Aug 21 2ʰ to Aug 23 13ʰ, and at other Fruit times, avoiding unfavourable times.

Immediately after harvest, sow catch crops like lupins, phacelia, mustard or wild flax.

Seeds for leaf plants: harvest at Leaf times, specially in the first half of the month.

Seeds for flower plants: at Flower times, specially in the second week of August.

Burn **fly papers** in the cow barn from Aug 17 16ʰ to Aug 19 13ʰ, and at other Flower times.

Ants in the house: burn when the Moon is in Leo, Aug 21 2ʰ to Aug 23 13ʰ, avoiding unfavourable times.

Biodynamic preparations: Cut **maple** and fill with dandelion and put it in the earth on Aug 15 from 8ʰ to 13ʰ.

Cut **yarrow** in the mornings at Flower times from Aug 11. The blossoms should show some seed formation.

Aug

▬▬▬▬ *Unfavourable time*   47

September 2017

Date	Const. of Moon	Solar & lunar aspects	Moon Trines	El'ment	Parts of the plant enhanced by Moon or planets	Weather

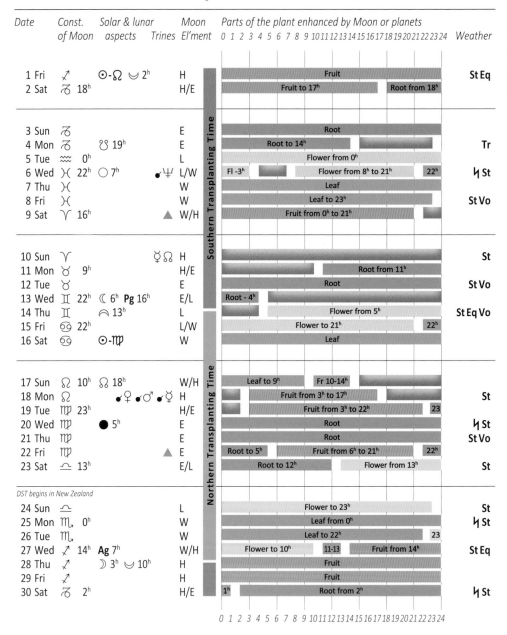

Date	Const. of Moon	Solar & lunar aspects	Moon Trines	El'ment	Weather
1 Fri	♐	☉-♌ ☽ 2ʰ		H	St Eq
2 Sat	♑ 18ʰ			H/E	
3 Sun	♑			E	
4 Mon	♑	☊ 19ʰ		E	Tr
5 Tue	♒ 0ʰ			L	
6 Wed	♓ 22ʰ	○ 7ʰ	♦♆	L/W	♄ St
7 Thu	♓			W	
8 Fri	♓			W	St Vo
9 Sat	♈ 16ʰ		▲	W/H	
10 Sun	♈		☿♌	H	St
11 Mon	♉ 9ʰ			H/E	
12 Tue	♉			E	St Vo
13 Wed	♊ 22ʰ	☾ 6ʰ **Pg** 16ʰ		E/L	
14 Thu	♊	⌢ 13ʰ		L	St Eq Vo
15 Fri	♋ 22ʰ			L/W	
16 Sat	♋	☉-♍		W	
17 Sun	♌ 10ʰ	♌ 18ʰ		W/H	
18 Mon	♌	♦♀ ♦♂ ♦☿		H	St
19 Tue	♍ 23ʰ			H/E	
20 Wed	♍	● 5ʰ		E	♄ St
21 Thu	♍			E	St Vo
22 Fri	♍		▲	E	
23 Sat	♎ 13ʰ			E/L	St
DST begins in New Zealand					
24 Sun	♎			L	St
25 Mon	♏ 0ʰ			W	♄ St
26 Tue	♏			W	
27 Wed	♐ 14ʰ **Ag** 7ʰ			W/H	St Eq
28 Thu	♐	☽ 3ʰ ☽ 10ʰ		H	
29 Fri	♐			H	
30 Sat	♑ 2ʰ			H/E	♄ St

	Mercury ☿	Venus ♀	Mars ♂	Jupiter ♃	Saturn ♄	Uranus ⛢	Neptune ♆	Pluto ♇
	♌ 26 ♍	♋	♌	♍	♏	♓	♒	♐
	(R 5 D)	10 ♌				(R)	(R)	(R 28 D)

NB: All zodiac symbols refer to astronomical constellations, not astrological signs (see p. 24)

1 ☽☌♇ 18ʰ
2 ♂△♁ 12ʰ

3 ☿☌♂ 10ʰ　☽☍♀ 16ʰ
4
5 ☽☍☿ 3ʰ　☽☍♂ 5ʰ　☉☍♆ 5ʰ
6 ☽●♆ 5ʰ
7
8
9 ☾☍♃ 5ʰ　☉△♇ 11ʰ　☾☌♁ 13ʰ

10 ☿♌ 21ʰ
11
12
13 ♀△♄ 1ʰ　☾☍♄ 8ʰ
14
15 ☾☍♇ 3ʰ
16 ☿☌♂ 19ʰ

17
18 ☾●♀ 1ʰ　♀△♁ 4ʰ　☾●♂ 20ʰ　☾●☿ 23ʰ
19 ☾☍♆ 3ʰ
20 ☿☍♆ 4ʰ
21
22 ☽☌♃ 10ʰ　☽☍♁ 13ʰ　☿△♇ 18ʰ
23

24 ♂☍♆ 20ʰ
25
26
27 ☽☌♄ 0ʰ
28 ♃☍♁ 4ʰ
29 ☽☌♇ 2ʰ
30 ♀☍♆ 0ʰ

The Warmth of August should last until Sep 25, as Mercury, Mars and Venus (from Sep 10) are in Leo, and should dominate the other planets in Water and Earth constellations.

Northern Transplanting Time
Sep 14 15ʰ to Sep 28 8ʰ
Southern Transplanting Time
Sep 1 4ʰ to Sep 14 11ʰ and
Sep 28 12ʰ to Oct 11

The times recommended for the **fruit harvest** are those in which the Moon is in Aries or Sagittarius (Aug 31 6ʰ to Sep 2 17ʰ, Sep 9 16ʰ to 21ʰ, and Sep 27 14ʰ to Sep 30 1ʰ) or other Fruit times.

The harvest of **root crops** is always best undertaken at Root times. Storage trials of onions, carrots, beetroot and potatoes have demonstrated this time and again.

Good times for **sowing winter grain** are when the Moon is in Leo or Sagittarius (Aug 31 6ʰ to Sep 2 17ʰ, Sep 17 10ʰ to Sep 19 22ʰ, and Sep 27 14ʰ to Sep 30 1ʰ) avoiding unfavourable times, and at other Fruit times.

Rye can if necessary also be sown at Root times with all subsequent cultivations being carried out at Fruit times.

Control slugs by burning between Sep 15 22ʰ and Sep 17 9ʰ.

Biodynamic preparations: Cut larch and fill with chamomile and put it in the earth on Sep 20 between 1ʰ and 9ʰ.

Planet (naked eye) visibility
Evening: Jupiter
All night: Saturn
Morning: Mercury (4th to 28th), Venus, Mars (from 11th)

Sep

▬▬▬ | *Unfavourable time*

49

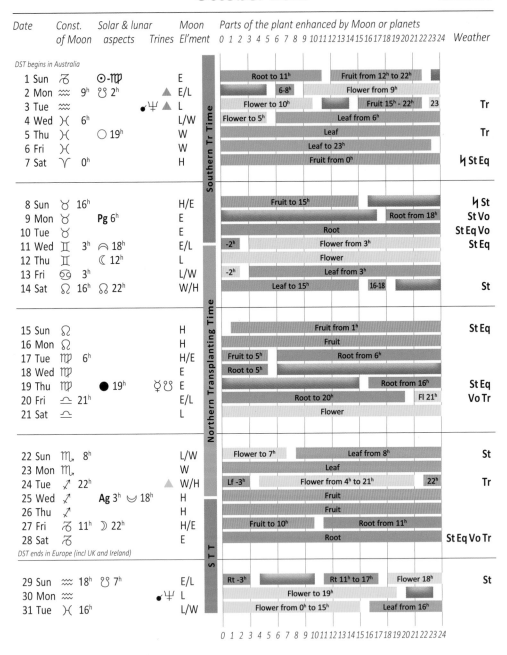

Date	Const. of Moon	Solar & lunar aspects	Moon Trines	El'ment	Parts of the plant enhanced by Moon or planets	Weather

DST begins in Australia

Southern Tr Time

1 Sun	♑	☉-♍		E	Root to 11ʰ / Fruit from 12ʰ to 22ʰ	
2 Mon	♒ 9ʰ	☊ 2ʰ	▲	E/L	6-8ʰ / Flower from 9ʰ	
3 Tue	♒		♂♆ ▲	L	Flower to 10ʰ / Fruit 15ʰ - 22ʰ 23	Tr
4 Wed	♓ 6ʰ			L/W	Flower to 5ʰ / Leaf from 6ʰ	Tr
5 Thu	♓	○ 19ʰ		W	Leaf	
6 Fri	♓			W	Leaf to 23ʰ	
7 Sat	♈ 0ʰ			H	Fruit from 0ʰ	♄ St Eq

8 Sun	♉ 16ʰ			H/E	Fruit to 15ʰ	♄ St
9 Mon	♉	**Pg** 6ʰ		E	Root from 18ʰ	St Vo
10 Tue	♉			E	Root	St Eq Vo
11 Wed	♊ 3ʰ	⌒ 18ʰ		E/L	-2ʰ / Flower from 3ʰ	St Eq
12 Thu	♊	☽ 12ʰ		L	Flower	
13 Fri	♋ 3ʰ			L/W	-2ʰ / Leaf from 3ʰ	
14 Sat	♌ 16ʰ	☊ 22ʰ		W/H	Leaf to 15ʰ 16-18	St

Northern Transplanting Time

15 Sun	♌			H	Fruit from 1ʰ	St Eq
16 Mon	♌			H	Fruit	
17 Tue	♍ 6ʰ			H/E	Fruit to 5ʰ / Root from 6ʰ	
18 Wed	♍			E	Root to 5ʰ	
19 Thu	♍	● 19ʰ	☿☊	E	Root from 16ʰ	St Eq
20 Fri	♎ 21ʰ			E/L	Root to 20ʰ Fl 21ʰ	Vo Tr
21 Sat	♎			L	Flower	

22 Sun	♏ 8ʰ			L/W	Flower to 7ʰ / Leaf from 8ʰ	St
23 Mon	♏			W	Leaf	
24 Tue	♐ 22ʰ		▲	W/H	Lf -3ʰ / Flower from 4ʰ to 21ʰ 22ʰ	Tr
25 Wed	♐	**Ag** 3ʰ ☋ 18ʰ		H	Fruit	
26 Thu	♐			H	Fruit	
27 Fri	♑ 11ʰ	☽ 22ʰ		H/E	Fruit to 10ʰ / Root from 11ʰ	
28 Sat	♑			E	Root	St Eq Vo Tr

DST ends in Europe (incl UK and Ireland)

S T T

29 Sun	♒ 18ʰ	☊ 7ʰ		E/L	Rt -3ʰ / Rt 11ʰ to 17ʰ Flower 18ʰ	St
30 Mon	♒		♂♆	L	Flower to 19ʰ	
31 Tue	♓ 16ʰ			L/W	Flower from 0ʰ to 15ʰ / Leaf from 16ʰ	

0 1 2 3 4 5 6 7 8 9 10 11 12 13 14 15 16 17 18 19 20 21 22 23 24

Mercury ☿	Venus ♀	Mars ♂	Jupiter ♃	Saturn ♄	Uranus ♅	Neptune ♆	Pluto ♇
♍	♌	♌	♍	♏	♓	♒	♐
23 ♎	9 ♍	12 ♍			(R)	(R)	

NB: All zodiac symbols refer to astronomical constellations, not astrological signs (see p. 24)

October 2017

1
2 ♂△♇ 0ʰ
3 ☽•♇ 13ʰ ♀△♇ 19ʰ ☽♂♀ 22ʰ
4 ☽♂♂ 0ʰ
5 ☽♂☿ 14ʰ ♀♂♂ 17ʰ
6 ☽♂☊ 19ʰ ☽♂♃ 23ʰ
7

8 ☉♂☿ 21ʰ
9
10 ☽♂♄ 16ʰ
11
12 ☽♂♇ 8ʰ
13
14

15 ☿♂☊ 8ʰ
16 ☽♂♆ 9ʰ
17 ☽♂♂ 11ʰ
18 ☽♂♀ 2ʰ ☿♂♃ 9ʰ
19 ☿☍ 4ʰ ☉♂☊ 17ʰ ☽♂☊ 19ʰ
20 ☽♂♃ 6ʰ ☽♂☿ 11ʰ
21

22
23
24 ☽♂♄ 12ʰ ☿△♆ 16ʰ
25
26 ☽♂♇ 11ʰ ☉♂♃ 18ʰ
27
28

29
30 ☽•♆ 22ʰ
31

Planet (naked eye) visibility
Evening: Jupiter (to 2nd), Saturn
All night:
Morning: Venus, Mars

October should be ideal for harvesting root crops. Sun, Mercury, Jupiter, Venus (from Oct 9) and Mars (from Oct 12) are all in the cool Earth constellation of Virgo. Other planets support with Water, Light and Warmth. Hopefully, the cool influences will not bring frost.

Northern Transplanting Time
Oct 11 20ʰ to Oct 25 16ʰ
Southern Transplanting Time
Sep 28 to Oct 11 16ʰ and
Oct 25 20ʰ to Nov 7

Store fruit at any Fruit or Flower time outside transplanting time.

Harvest seeds of root plants at Root times, **seeds for leaf plants** at Leaf times, and **seeds for flower plants** at Flower times.

All **cleared ground** should be treated with compost and sprayed with barrel preparation, and ploughed ready for winter.

Control slugs by burning between Oct 13 3ʰ and Oct 14 15ʰ.

Cider press

Unfavourable time   51

November 2017

Date	Const. of Moon	Solar & lunar aspects	Moon Trines	El'ment	Parts of the plant enhanced by Moon or planets 0 1 2 3 4 5 6 7 8 9 10 11 12 13 14 15 16 17 18 19 20 21 22 23 24	Weather

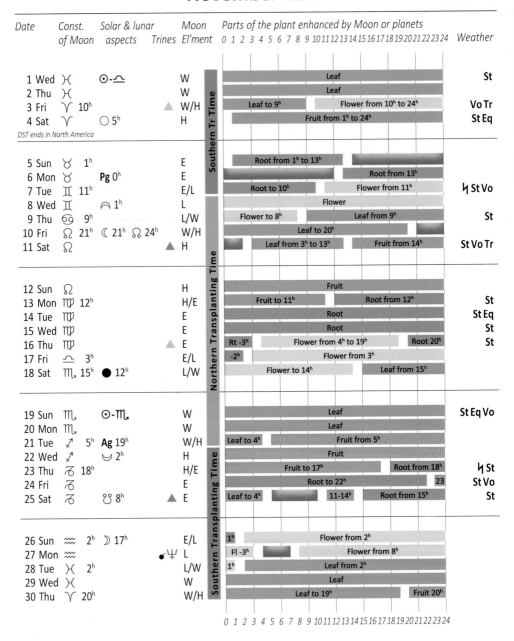

Southern Tr Time

1 Wed ♓	☉-♎	W		Leaf	St
2 Thu ♓		W		Leaf	
3 Fri ♈ 10ʰ		▲ W/H		Leaf to 9ʰ · Flower from 10ʰ to 24ʰ	Vo Tr
4 Sat ♈	○ 5ʰ	H		Fruit from 1ʰ to 24ʰ	St Eq

DST ends in North America

5 Sun ♉ 1ʰ		E		Root from 1ʰ to 13ʰ	
6 Mon ♉	Pg 0ʰ	E		Root from 13ʰ	
7 Tue ♊ 11ʰ		E/L		Root to 10ʰ · Flower from 11ʰ	♄ St Vo
8 Wed ♊	⚺ 1ʰ	L		Flower	
9 Thu ♋ 9ʰ		L/W		Flower to 8ʰ · Leaf from 9ʰ	St
10 Fri ♌ 21ʰ	☾ 21ʰ ♌ 24ʰ	W/H		Leaf to 20ʰ	
11 Sat ♌		▲ H		Leaf from 3ʰ to 13ʰ · Fruit from 14ʰ	St Vo Tr

Northern Transplanting Time

12 Sun ♌		H		Fruit	
13 Mon ♍ 12ʰ		H/E		Fruit to 11ʰ · Root from 12ʰ	St
14 Tue ♍		E		Root	St Eq
15 Wed ♍		E		Root	St
16 Thu ♍		▲ E		Rt -3ʰ · Flower from 4ʰ to 19ʰ · Root 20ʰ	St
17 Fri ♎ 3ʰ	● 12ʰ	E/L		-2ʰ · Flower from 3ʰ	
18 Sat ♏ 15ʰ	● 12ʰ	L/W		Flower to 14ʰ · Leaf from 15ʰ	

19 Sun ♏	☉-♏	W		Leaf	St Eq Vo
20 Mon ♏		W		Leaf	
21 Tue ♐ 5ʰ	Ag 19ʰ	W/H		Leaf to 4ʰ · Fruit from 5ʰ	
22 Wed ♐	⚮ 2ʰ	H		Fruit	
23 Thu ♑ 18ʰ		H/E		Fruit to 17ʰ · Root from 18ʰ	♄ St
24 Fri ♑		E		Root to 22ʰ · 23	St Vo
25 Sat ♑	☍ 8ʰ	▲ E		Leaf to 4ʰ · 11-14ʰ · Root from 15ʰ	St

Southern Transplanting Time

26 Sun ♒ 2ʰ	☽ 17ʰ	E/L		1ʰ · Flower from 2ʰ	
27 Mon ♒	•♆	L		Fl -3ʰ · Flower from 8ʰ	
28 Tue ♓ 2ʰ		L/W		1ʰ · Leaf from 2ʰ	
29 Wed ♓		W		Leaf	
30 Thu ♈ 20ʰ		W/H		Leaf to 19ʰ · Fruit 20ʰ	

0 1 2 3 4 5 6 7 8 9 10 11 12 13 14 15 16 17 18 19 20 21 22 23 24

Mercury ☿	Venus ♀	Mars ♂	Jupiter ♃	Saturn ♄	Uranus ♅	Neptune ♆	Pluto ♇
♎ 4 ♏	♍ 15 ♎	♍	♍	♏	♓	♒	♐
30 ♐	29 ♏		24 ♎		(R)	(R 22 D)	

NB: All zodiac symbols refer to astronomical constellations, not astrological signs (see p. 24)

Planetary aspects
*(**Bold** = visible to naked eye)*

1	☽ ☍ ♂ 18ʰ
2	
3	☽ ☍ ♀ 1ʰ ☽ ☌ ☊ 3ʰ ☽ ☍ ♃ 18ʰ ☉ △ ♆ 19ʰ
4	♀ ☍ ☊ 5ʰ
5	☾ ☍ ☿ 9ʰ
6	
7	☾ ☍ ♄ 3ʰ
8	☾ ☍ ♇ 15ʰ
9	
10	
11	♄ △ ☊ 9ʰ
12	☾ ☍ ♆ 13ʰ
13	♀ ☌ ♃ 8ʰ
14	
15	☾ ☌ ♂ 3ʰ
16	☾ ☍ ☊ 0ʰ ♀ △ ♆ 15ʰ
17	☾ ☌ ♃ 0ʰ ☾ ☌ ♀ 8ʰ
18	
19	
20	☽ ☌ ☿ 11ʰ
21	☽ ☌ ♄ 0ʰ
22	☽ ☌ ♇ 19ʰ
23	
24	
25	☿ △ ☊ 11ʰ
26	
27	☽ ● ♆ 6ʰ
28	☿ ☌ ♄ 7ʰ
29	
30	☽ ☍ ♂ 11ʰ ☽ ☌ ☊ 12ʰ

Planet (naked eye) visibility
Evening: Saturn
All night:
Morning: Venus, Mars, Jupiter (from 8th)

The Sun moves into Libra on November 1, and into Scorpio on Nov 19. The planets move alternately in Water and Earth constellations, with occasional Light and Warmth times, giving a colourful mix.

Northern Transplanting Time
Nov 8 3ʰ to Nov 21 24ʰ
Southern Transplanting Time
Oct 25 to Nov 7 23ʰ and
Nov 22 4ʰ to Dec 5

The Flower times in Transplanting Time are ideal for **planting flower bulbs,** showing vigorous growth and vivid colours. The remaining Flower times should only be considered as back up, as bulbs planted on those times will not flower so freely.

If not already completed in October, all organic waste materials should be gathered and made into a **compost.** Applying the biodynamic preparations to the compost will ensure a rapid transformation and good fungal development. An application of barrel preparation will also help the composting process.

Fruit and forest trees will also benefit at this time from a spraying of horn manure and/or barrel preparation when being transplanted.

Best times for **cutting Advent greenery** and **Christmas trees** for transporting are Flower times outside Transplanting Time (Nov 3 10ʰ to 24ʰ, Nov 7 11ʰ to Nov 8 3ʰ and Nov 26 2ʰ to Nov 28 1ʰ).

Burn **fly papers** in cow barn at Flower times, Nov 7 11ʰ to Nov 9 8ʰ and Nov 17 3ʰ to Nov 18 14ʰ.

Biodynamic preparations: Put birch and yarrow into the ground on Nov 4 3ʰ to 11ʰ.

Nov

▬▬▬ *Unfavourable time*

December 2017

Date	Const. of Moon	Solar & lunar aspects	Trines	Moon El'ment	Parts of the plant enhanced by Moon or planets	Weather

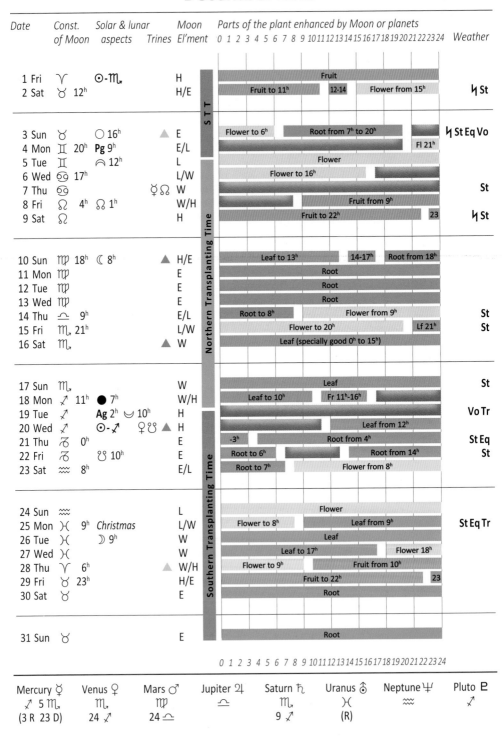

Date	Const. of Moon	Solar & lunar aspects	Trines	Moon El'ment	Plant parts	Weather
1 Fri	♈	☉-♏		H	Fruit	
2 Sat	♉ 12ʰ			H/E	Fruit to 11ʰ / 12-14 / Flower from 15ʰ	♄ St
3 Sun	♉	○ 16ʰ	▲	E	Flower to 6ʰ / Root from 7ʰ to 20ʰ	♄ St Eq Vo
4 Mon	♊ 20ʰ	Pg 9ʰ		E/L	Fl 21ʰ	
5 Tue	♊	⌒ 12ʰ		L	Flower	
6 Wed	♋ 17ʰ			L/W	Flower to 16ʰ	
7 Thu	♋		☿♌	W		St
8 Fri	♌ 4ʰ	♌ 1ʰ		W/H	Fruit from 9ʰ	
9 Sat	♌			H	Fruit to 22ʰ / 23	♄ St
10 Sun	♍ 18ʰ	☾ 8ʰ	▲	H/E	Leaf to 13ʰ / 14-17ʰ / Root from 18ʰ	
11 Mon	♍			E	Root	
12 Tue	♍			E	Root	
13 Wed	♍			E	Root	
14 Thu	♎ 9ʰ			E/L	Root to 8ʰ / Flower from 9ʰ	St
15 Fri	♏ 21ʰ			L/W	Flower to 20ʰ / Lf 21ʰ	St
16 Sat	♏		▲	W	Leaf (specially good 0ʰ to 15ʰ)	
17 Sun	♏			W	Leaf	St
18 Mon	♐ 11ʰ	● 7ʰ		W/H	Leaf to 10ʰ / Fr 11ʰ-16ʰ	
19 Tue	♐	Ag 2ʰ ☋ 10ʰ		H		Vo Tr
20 Wed	♐	☉-♐	♀☍ ▲	H	Leaf from 12ʰ	St Eq
21 Thu	♑ 0ʰ			E	-3ʰ / Root from 4ʰ	St Eq
22 Fri	♑	☍ 10ʰ		E	Root to 6ʰ / Root from 14ʰ	St
23 Sat	♒ 8ʰ			E/L	Root to 7ʰ / Flower from 8ʰ	
24 Sun	♒			L	Flower	
25 Mon	♓ 9ʰ	*Christmas*		L/W	Flower to 8ʰ / Leaf from 9ʰ	St Eq Tr
26 Tue	♓	☽ 9ʰ		W	Leaf	
27 Wed	♓			W	Leaf to 17ʰ / Flower 18ʰ	
28 Thu	♈ 6ʰ		▲	W/H	Flower to 9ʰ / Fruit from 10ʰ	
29 Fri	♉ 23ʰ			H/E	Fruit to 22ʰ / 23	
30 Sat	♉			E	Root	
31 Sun	♉			E	Root	

0 1 2 3 4 5 6 7 8 9 10 11 12 13 14 15 16 17 18 19 20 21 22 23 24

Mercury ☿	Venus ♀	Mars ♂	Jupiter ♃	Saturn ♄	Uranus ♅	Neptune ♆	Pluto ♇
♐ 5 ♏	♏	♍	♎	♏	♓	♒	♐
(3 R 23 D)	24 ♐	24 ♎		9 ♐	(R)		

NB: All zodiac symbols refer to astronomical constellations, not astrological signs (see p. 24)

Planetary aspects
*(**Bold** = visible to naked eye)*

1	♂☌☊ 10ʰ ☽☍♃ 15ʰ
2	
3	☽☍♀ 1ʰ ♃△♆ 3ʰ
4	☾☌♄ 18ʰ ☾☍☿ 19ʰ
5	
6	☾☍♇ 1ʰ ☿☌♄ 12ʰ
7	☿☊ 20ʰ
8	
9	☾☍♆ 20ʰ
10	☿△☊ 10ʰ
11	
12	
13	☉☌☿ 2ʰ ☾☍☊ 4ʰ ☾☌♂ 19ʰ
14	☾☌♃ 17ʰ
15	☿☌♀ 14ʰ
16	☉△☊ 11ʰ
17	☾☌☿ 9ʰ ☾☌♀ 19ʰ
18	☽☌♄ 13ʰ
19	
20	♀☋ 0ʰ ☽☌♇ 3ʰ ♀△☊ 23ʰ
21	☉☌♄ 21ʰ
22	
23	
24	☽☌♆ 14ʰ
25	♀☌♄ 18ʰ
26	
27	☽☌☊ 21ʰ
28	♂△♆ 6ʰ
29	☽☍♂ 4ʰ ☽☍♃ 10ʰ
30	
31	☽☍☿ 13ʰ

Planet (naked eye) visibility
Evening: Saturn (to 4th)
All night:
Morning: Venus (to 9th), Mars, Jupiter

December continues with a colourful mix. Mercury and Venus interchange between warm Sagittarius and watery Scorpio. Mars in Virgo brings cold, and Jupiter strengthens Light influences. With Saturn moving from a Water to a Warmth constellation, Uranus bringing Water influences, Neptune in Light and Pluto in Warmth, it is unlikely to be a white Christmas.

Northern Transplanting Time
Dec 5 14ʰ to Dec 19 8ʰ
Southern Transplanting Time
Nov 22 to Dec 5 10ʰ and
Dec 19 12ʰ to Jan 1

The transplanting time is good for **pruning trees and hedges.** Fruit trees should be pruned at Fruit or Flower times.

Best times for cutting **Advent greenery** and **Christmas trees** are at Flower times to ensure lasting fragrance.

Burn feathers or skins of **warm blooded pests** from Dec 2 12ʰ to Dec 3 20ʰ. Ensure the fire is glowing hot (don't use grilling charcoal). Lay dry feathers or skins on the glowing embers. After they have cooled, collect the light grey ash and grind for an hour with a pestle and mortar. This increases the efficacy and the ash can be potentised later. *The burning and grinding should be completed by Dec 3 20ʰ.*

Southern hemisphere:
Harvest time for seeds (avoid unfavourable times):
Leaf seeds: Leaf times.
Fruit seeds: Fruit times, preferably with Moon in Leo (Dec 8 9ʰ to Dec 9 22ʰ).
Root seeds: Root times.
Flower seeds: Flower times.

Control slugs Dec 6 17ʰ to Dec 8 3ʰ.

We wish all our readers a blessed Advent and Christmastide and the best of health for the New Year of 2018

Sowing times for trees and shrubs

March 24: Apple, Beech, Alder
April 21: Apple, Beech, Ash, Sweet chestnut
June 15 (after 11^h): Alder, Larch, Lime tree, Elm, Thuja, Juniper, Plum, Hornbeam
June 30: Pear, Birch, Lime tree, Robinia, Willow
July 10: Ash, Cedar, Fir, Spruce, Hazel
July 24: Birch, Pear, Lime tree, Robinia, Willow, Thuja, Juniper, Plum, Hornbeam
Sep 9: Ash, Cedar, Fir, Spruce, Hazel
Sep 20: Alder, Larch, Lime tree, Elm
Oct 19 (after 16^h): Ash, Spruce, Hazel, Fir, Cedar
Dec 1: Yew, Oak, Cherry, Horse chestnut (buckeye), Sweet chestnut, Spruce, Fir, Thuja, Juniper, Hornbeam

The above dates refer to sowing times of the seeds. They are not times for transplanting already existing plants.

The dates given are based on planetary aspects, which create particularly favourable growing conditions for the species in question. For trees and shrubs not mentioned above, sow at an appropriate time of the Moon's position in the zodiac, depending on the part of the tree or shrub to be enhanced. Avoid unfavourable times.

Felling times for timber

June 3: Maple, Apple, Copper beech, Sweet chestnut, Walnut, Spruce, Hornbeam, Pine, Fir, Thuja, Cedar, Plum, Plum, Alder, Larch, Lime tree, Elm, Birch, Pear, Robinia, Willow
June 28: Alder, Larch, Lime tree, Elm
July 18: Birch, Pear, Larch, Lime tree, Robinia, Willow
Oct 24: Alder, Larch, Lime tree, Elm
Nov 3: Ash, Spruce, Hazel, Fir, Cedar
Dec 21: Birch, Pear, Larch, Lime tree, Robinia, Willow

Those trees which are not listed should be felled during November and December at Flower times during the descending Moon period (transplanting time). Avoid unfavourable times.

Types of crop

Flower plants

artichoke
broccoli
flower bulbs
flowering ornamental shrubs
flowers
flowery herbs
rose
sunflower

Leaf plants

asparagus
Brussels sprouts
cabbage
cauliflower
celery
chard
chicory (endive)
Chinese cabbage (pe-tsai)
corn salad (lamb's lettuce)
crisphead (iceberg) lettuce
curly kale (green cabbage)
endive (chicory)
finocchio (Florence fennel)
green cabbage (curly kale)
iceberg (crisphead) lettuce
kohlrabi
lamb's lettuce (corn salad)
leaf herbs
leek
lettuce
pe-tsai (Chinese cabbage)
red cabbage
rhubarb
shallots
spinach

Root plants

beetroot
black (Spanish) salsify
carrot
celeriac
garlic
horseradish
Jerusalem artichoke
parsnip
potato
radish
red radish
root tubers
Spanish (black) salsify

Fruit plants

aubergine (eggplant)
bush bean
courgette (zucchini)
cucumber
eggplant (aubergine)
grains
lentil
maize
melon
paprika
pea
pumpkin (squash)
runner bean
soya
squash (pumpkin)
tomato
zucchini (courgette)

The care of bees

A colony of bees lives in its hive closed off from the outside world. For extra protection against harmful influences, the inside of the hive is sealed with propolis. The link with the wider surroundings is made by the bees that fly in and out of the hive.

To make good use of cosmic rhythms, the beekeeper needs to create the right conditions in much the same way as the gardener or farmer does with the plants. The gardener works the soil and in so doing allows cosmic forces to penetrate it via the air. These forces can then be taken up and used by the plants until the soil is next moved.

When the beekeeper opens up the hive, the sealing layer of propolis is broken. This creates a disturbance, as a result of which cosmic forces can enter and influence the life of the hive until the next intervention by the beekeeper. By this means the beekeeper can directly mediate cosmic forces to the bees.

It is not insignificant which forces of the universe are brought into play when the the hive is opened. The beekeeper can consciously intervene by choosing days for working with the hive that will help the colony to develop and build up its food reserves. The bees will then reward the beekeeper by providing a portion of their harvest in the form of honey.

Earth-Root times can be selected for opening the hive if the bees need to do more building. Light-Flower times encourage brood activity and colony development. Warmth-Fruit times stimulate the collection of nectar. Water-Leaf times are unsuitable for working in the hive or for the removal and processing of honey.

Since the late 1970s the varroa mite has affected virtually every bee colony in Europe. Following a number of comparative trials we recommend burning and making an ash of the varroa mite in the usual way. After dynamising it for one hour, the ash should be put in a salt-cellar and sprinkled lightly between the combs. The ash should be made and sprinkled when the Sun and Moon are in Taurus (May/June).

Feeding bees in preparation for winter

The herbal teas recommended as supplements in the feeding of bees prior to winter are all plants that have proved their value over many years. Yarrow, chamomile, dandelion and valerian are made by pouring boiling water over the flowers, allowing them to brew for fifteen minutes and then straining them. Stinging nettle, horsetail and oak bark are placed in cold water, brought slowly to the boil and simmered for fifteen minutes. Three grams (1 tablespoon) of each dried herb and half a litre (½ quart) of the prepared teas is enough to produce 100 litres (25 gal) of liquid feed. This is a particularly important treatment in years when there are large amounts of honeydew.

Fungal problems

The function of fungus in nature is to break down dying organic materials. It appears amongst our crops when unripe manure compost or uncomposted animal by-products such as horn and bone meal are used but also when seeds are harvested during unfavourable constellations: according to Steiner, 'When Moon forces are working too strongly on the Earth ...'

Tea can be made from horsetail (*Equisetum arvense*) and sprayed on to the soil where affected plants are growing. This draws the fungal level back down into the ground where it belongs.

The plants can be strengthened by spraying stinging nettle tea on the leaves. This will promote good assimilation, stimulate the flow of sap and help fungal diseases to disappear.

Biodynamic preparation plants

Pick **dandelions** in the morning at Flower times as soon as they are open and while the centre of the flowers are still tightly packed.

Pick **yarrow** at Fruit times when the Sun is in Leo (around the middle of August).

Pick **chamomile** at Flower times just before midsummer. If they are harvested too late, seeds will begin to form and there are often grubs in the hollow heads.

Collect **stinging nettles** when the first flowers are opening, usually around midsummer. Harvest the whole plants without roots at Flower times.

Pick **valerian** at Flower times around midsummer.

All the flowers (except valerian) should be laid out on paper and dried in the shade.

Collect **oak bark** at Root times. The pithy material below the bark should not be used.

Biodynamic preparations: putting birch and yarrow into the ground

Moon diagrams

The diagrams overleaf show for each month the daily position (evenings GMT) of the Moon against the stars and other planets. For viewing in the southern hemisphere, turn the diagrams upside down.

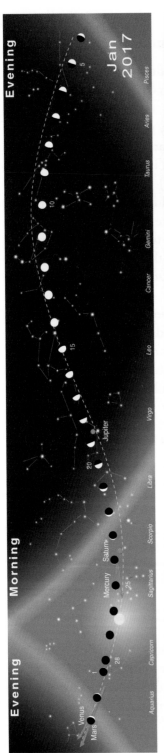

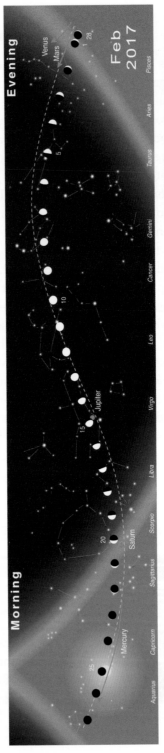

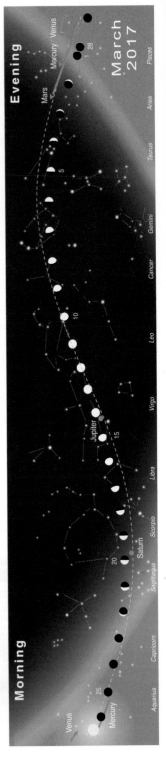

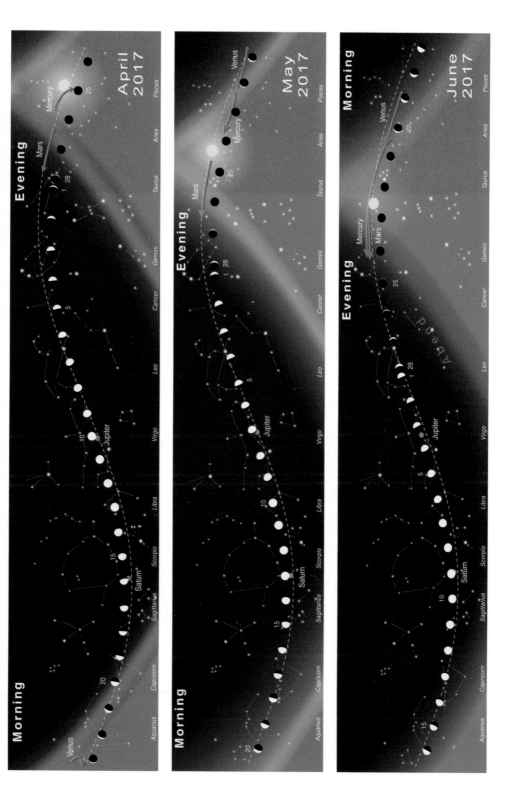

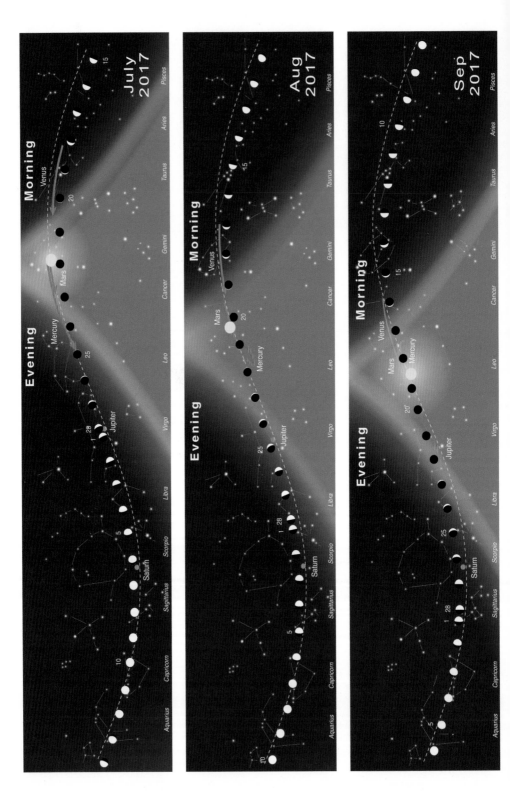

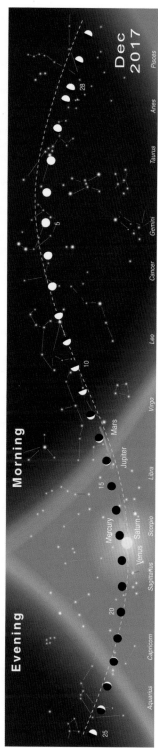

63

Further Reading

Colquhoun, Margaret and Axel Ewald, *New Eyes for Plants,* Hawthorn

Karlsson, Britt and Per, *Biodynamic, Organic and Natural Winemaking,* Floris

Klett, Manfred, *Principles of Biodynamic Spray and Compost Preparations,* Floris

Koepf, H.H., *Koepf's Practical Biodynamics: Soil, Compost, Sprays and Food Quality,* Floris

Kranich, Ernst Michael, *Planetary Influences upon Plants,* Biodynamic Association, USA

Lepetit, Antoine, *What's so Special About Biodynamic Wine?* Floris

Masson, Pierre, *A Biodynamic Manual,* Floris

Morrow, Joel, *Vegetable Gardening for Organic and Biodynamic Growers,* Lindisfarne

Osthaus, Karl-Ernst, *The Biodynamic Farm,* Floris

Pfeiffer, Ehrenfried, *The Earth's Face,* Lanthorn

—, *Pfeiffer's Introduction to Biodynamics,* Floris

—, *Weeds and What They Tell Us,* Floris

—, & Michael Maltas, *The Biodynamic Orchard Book,* Floris

Philbrick, John and Helen, *Gardening for Health and Nutrition,* Anthroposophic, USA

Philbrick, Helen & Gregg, Richard B., *Companion Plants and How to Use Them,* Floris

Sattler, Friedrich & Eckard von Wistinghausen, *Growing Biodynamic Crops,* Floris

Schilthuis, Willy, *Biodynamic Agriculture,* Floris

Steiner, Rudolf, *Agriculture (A Course of Eight Lectures),* Biodynamic Association, USA

—, *Agriculture: An Introductory Reader,* Steiner Press, UK

—, *What is Biodynamics? A Way to Heal and Revitalize the Earth,* SteinerBooks, USA

Storl, Wolf, *Culture and Horticulture,* North Atlantic Books, USA

Thun, Maria, *Gardening for Life,* Hawthorn

—, *The Biodynamic Year,* Temple Lodge

Thun, Matthias, *When Wine Tastes Best: A Biodynamic Calendar for Wine Drinkers,* (annual) Floris

von Keyserlink, Adelbert Count, *The Birth of a New Agriculture,* Temple Lodge

—, *Developing Biodynamic Agriculture,* Temple Lodge

Waldin, Monty, *Monty Waldin's Best Biodynamic Wines,* Floris

Weiler, Michael, *Bees and Honey, from Flower to Jar,* Floris

Wright, Hilary, *Biodynamic Gardening for Health and Taste,* Floris

Biodynamic Associations

Demeter International
www.demeter.net
Australia:
Bio-Dynamic Research Institute
www.demeter.org.au
Biodynamic Agriculture Australia
www.biodynamics.net.au
Canada: Society for Bio-Dynamic Farming & Gardening in Ontario
biodynamics.on.ca
India: Bio-Dynamic Association of India (BDAI)
www.biodynamics.in

New Zealand:
Biodynamic Association
www.biodynamic.org.nz
South Africa: Biodynamic Agricultural Association of Southern Africa
www.bdaasa.org.za
UK: Biodynamic Association
www.biodynamic.org.uk
USA: Biodynamic Association
www.biodynamics.com